SIMPLE SE...
BLOC...

D0512251

Other Titles of Interest

SIMPLE SENSOR TERMINAL BLOCK PROJECTS

by

R. BEBBINGTON

BERNARD BABANI (publishing) LTD
THE GRAMPIANS
SHEPHERDS BUSH ROAD
LONDON W6 7NF
ENGLAND

Please Note

Although every care has been taken with the production of this book to ensure that any projects, designs, modifications and/or programs, etc., contained herewith, operate in a correct and safe manner and also that any components specified are normally available in Great Britain, the Publishers do not accept responsibility in any way for the failure, including fault in design, of any project, design, modification or program to work correctly or to cause damage to any other equipment that it may be connected to or used in conjunction with, or in respect of any other damage or injury that may be so caused, nor do the Publishers accept responsibility in any way for the failure to obtain specified components.

Notice is also given that if equipment that is still under warranty is modified in any way or used or connected with home-built equipment then that warranty may be void.

© 1997 BERNARD BABANI (publishing) LTD

First Published – August 1997

British Library Cataloguing in Publication Data

A catalogue record for this book is available from the British Library

ISBN 0 85934 432 0

Cover Design by Gregor Arthur

Printed and bound in Great Britain by Cox & Wyman Ltd, Reading

Preface

This book is the next logical step from BP378 *45 Simple Electronic Terminal Block Projects*, by the same author and publisher as this book, which describes an easy method of constructing transistor circuits without the need for soldering – an 'open sesame' to the practical world of electronics for youngsters or beginners. Having mastered a number of basic circuits using discrete components, these projects provide 'hands on' experience with some popular integrated circuits (IC), again using the plastic screw-terminal blocks, widely referred to by electricians as 'chocolate blocks'.

Although integrated circuits are more ambitious than single transistor circuits, as most of the components are packed in the ICs, the external wiring required is often simpler. For instance, twenty-three transistors, two diodes and sixteen resistors are packed in the 'centimetric' 555 timer IC used for a number of these projects. Integrated circuits are not only much smaller than their discrete counterparts, but demand far less current. Consequently, all projects are battery-powered, an essential safety feature for beginners.

Not all the external components are obligingly supplied with wire ends that will push into a terminal block so the constructor must prevail upon a friend or relative to do some initial soldering if hot irons are declared a 'no-go' area. Full instructions on making up the IC-breadboards are given in Chapter 2 BASIC COMPONENTS AND CONNECTIONS.

Armed with a layout diagram showing the actual physical shape of the components and instructions, most projects can be constructed within a matter of minutes. A small list of components is found at the end of each project, made up from a nucleus of common items, allowing them to be re-used for many other projects.

Many circuits can be easily modified for experimentation, or extended as modular units. Since the wire ends do not have to be cut and soldered, external components can be used again and again.

Typically, battery supplies and holders are fitted with wire-ended clips. However, components that are not wire-ended, for example, potentiometers, loudspeakers, thyristors, etc., can be wire-wrapped, or better still, soldered if possible. Short, flexible leads on these few components will pay dividends when you come to connect them into the terminal block projects.

As the book is also aimed at younger readers and beginners, simplified instructions are given for those not familiar with electrical and electronic components and circuits.

In addition to the block wiring layout showing the physical arrangement and connections, the circuit diagram is included to familiarise readers with component symbols and circuit conventions.

Roy Bebbington

Contents

Chapter 1

SENSING AND SYSTEMS

Three centuries ago, an Englishman, John Locke arrived at the conclusion that nothing is in the mind that was not first in the senses. We sense, reflect, and depending on what our senses tell us, we spring into action to apply our knowledge and ideas. As our human systems rely on our senses, similarly, also many electronic systems are activated by sensing and transducing devices.

A sensor is defined as a device used to *detect or measure* a physical quantity, for instance, sound, light, temperature, pressure, magnetic field strength, etc. In electrical sensors, the varying output, usually a voltage or a current, corresponds to that of the physical quantity applied.

A transducer is defined as a device that *converts* one form of energy into another. In electronics, transducers are regarded as devices that change a non-electrical physical quantity into an electrical signal, or vice versa; for instance, a microphone and a loudspeaker. If the transducer takes energy from the physical quantity, e.g. a passive component such as light-dependent resistor (LDR), strictly speaking it should be referred to as a sensor. Having said that, some sensors are also transducers, and the names for some of the devices tend to confuse the issue. However, 'a rose by any other name will smell just as sweet'. Not applicable to the gas detector of Chapter 9, it could hardly be described as a perfume detector!

An electronic system is an orderly 'cause and effect' arrangement of basic blocks, with inputs and outputs as indicated in Figure 1. The input of a system is processed to effect a change of output. The output change might be made to trigger an alarm, light a lamp, turn a motor, deflect a meter needle, or operate a mechanical device, etc.

The diagram lists some of the sensors, circuit blocks and outputs that could be used in an electronic system. Primarily, it is the method of sensing that we are interested in here, and how best we can use the sensor to control or drive a system so that it gives the desired output effect.

1

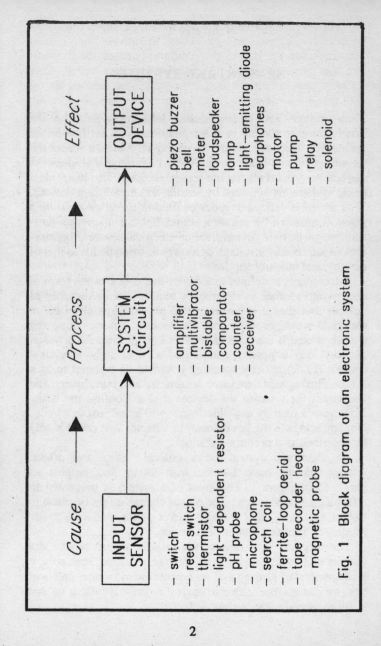

Fig. 1 Block diagram of an electronic system

INPUT SENSOR
- switch
- reed switch
- thermistor
- light-dependent resistor
- pH probe
- microphone
- search coil
- ferrite-loop aerial
- tape recorder head
- magnetic probe

Cause

SYSTEM (circuit)
- amplifier
- multivibrator
- bistable
- comparator
- counter
- receiver

Process

OUTPUT DEVICE
- piezo buzzer
- bell
- meter
- loudspeaker
- lamp
- light-emitting diode
- earphones
- motor
- pump
- relay
- solenoid

Effect

Like our human senses, we can use touch, sight, sound, and to a lesser degree smell and taste, to provide inputs to an electronic system. If from this handful of senses, the scope for projects appears to be limited, we should reflect that the sense of touch, for instance, conjures up such input devices as contact, touch and pressure switches, microswitches, temperature sensitive resistors, thermostats; sight suggests light, with inputs such as photo-transistors, opto-couplers, solar cells, infra-red detectors, and light-dependent resistors. In addition to the human sense mentioned, electronic devices can respond to magnetic- and electro-magnetic-activated sensors.

From the list, it is obvious that there is a wide range of sensors to choose from. Which one you select will depend upon what you want to detect or control. Having selected a suitable sensor to detect a required input, the next step is to dream up a practical system for it to operate. The projects that follow each chapter indicate a variety of ways in which a sensor can be used as an input to a system to produce a suitable output. With the input signal sensed correctly, many systems are flexible enough or can be adapted to control a range of output devices such as lights, buzzers and relays.

Chapter 2

BASIC COMPONENTS AND CONNECTIONS

A big advantage for those taking up practical electronics as a hobby, especially youngsters with little cash to spare, is that a number of different projects can be constructed using the same basic components. Moreover when these components are connected by terminal blocks, it is a simple matter to take them apart and use them over and over again in other circuits. For this reason, the number of components used throughout these projects has been kept to a minimum.

Basic Components

Glance through the circuit diagrams or component lists in this book, or in any of the many electronics project books available, and you will come across the mysterious code letters R, C, L, LS, TR, IC, etc. The seasoned electronics enthusiasts will know all about these, but for the sake of newcomers, and those who need a little memory-jogging, it is useful to be able to recognise these basic components and to know something about their functions in an electronic system. There are now some catalogues on sale in the larger stationers that give details about electronic components, but here is a short description of the most common components that you will find in the following projects.

Batteries (BY1 ...) – drivers of electricity

All the projects listed in this book can be powered by low-voltage batteries; a number of dry cells connected in series. A single cell produces a driving force of 1.5 volts. Most of the projects listed work perfectly well on a 9-volt layer-type battery such as the familiar PP3 as shown in Figure 2. However, where heavier currents are taken by a circuit, a larger version, a PP6 or PP9 battery would offer longer life. Alternatively, for circuits in constant use, the tubular 1.5V carbon-zinc AA cells, as used in torches, offer a better solution. As you will realise by simple

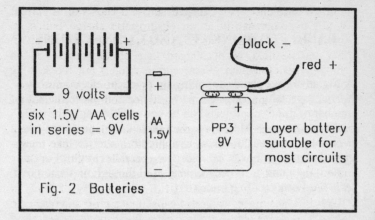

Fig. 2 Batteries

9 volts

six 1.5V AA cells in series = 9V

AA 1.5V

black —
red +

PP3 9V

Layer battery suitable for most circuits

arithmetic, six of these cells give 9 volts. These batteries can be made up by clipping the AA cells into plastic battery holders, commercially available. Battery holders are either equipped with two connecting leads or snap-on clips.

The battery can be regarded as an electrical pump, capable of forcing electrical current (the movement of *electrons*) around a circuit. The higher the voltage of the battery, the more current will flow.

Capacitors (C1 . . .) – storers of electricity

Shown in Figure 3, a capacitor basically consists of two metal foil plates, rolled up for convenience, with the *dielectric*, an insulating material such as plastic, between them. The larger the area of the plates, the larger the capacitance. If a battery, or

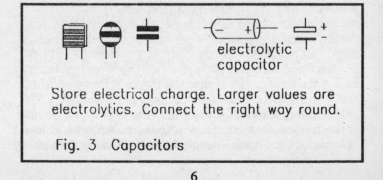

electrolytic capacitor

Store electrical charge. Larger values are electrolytics. Connect the right way round.

Fig. 3 Capacitors

voltage difference, is connected across a capacitor, a current will flow momentarily as an electrostatic charge builds up across the plates. This charge is stored (exploited in Project 30) and can be held, or discharged in a circuit, depending on the required function. Direct currents (d.c.) are blocked by capacitors, but alternating currents (a.c.) are allowed to flow, depending on the value of the capacitor and the frequency of the signals.

The unit of capacitance is the farad, but this is far too large for practical use. Capacitors are therefore measured in microfarads (μF), millionths of a farad, nanofarads (nF), thousandths of a microfarad, or picofarads (pF), thousandths of a nanofarad. For example, a capacitor of 0.01μF is equivalent to 10nF or 10,000pF. The bigger values of capacitance (1μF and over) are usually provided by electrolytic capacitors; these are polarised and must be connected with the + sign towards the positive side of the circuit.

Resistors (R1 . . .) – controllers of electricity
A resistor, measured in ohms, kilohms (kΩ) and megohms (MΩ), depending on its value, offers a certain resistance to the flow of current in a circuit (Fig.4a). By controlling the electron flow, resistors limit the currents and voltages in a circuit to required levels. For instance, variable resistors, or potentiometers (Fig.4b) can be used to adjust voltages or volume levels in radios and amplifiers, mix microphone inputs in tape recorders, etc. The value of a fixed resistor is usually indicated on its cylindrical body by three coloured bands at one end, as shown in the figure. The coloured bands refer to the values of the 1st and 2nd significant figures and the number of noughts that follow. For instance, the table indicates that if the first band is red, the most-significant figure is 2. If the second band is violet, the second-significant figure is 7. If the third band is orange, the number of noughts is three; the value of the resistor is 27,000 ohms (27k). A fourth band at the other end of the resistor denotes tolerance: brown ±1%, red ±2%, gold ±5% and silver ±10%.

Conductors – movers of electricity
Copper wire is usually used to conduct electricity around a circuit, and the shorter and thicker the wire, the greater will be

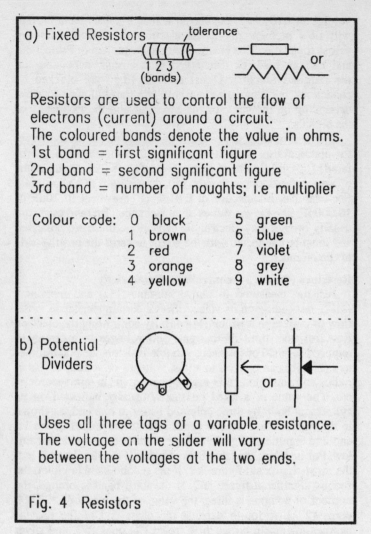

a) Fixed Resistors

tolerance

1 2 3
(bands)

or

Resistors are used to control the flow of
electrons (current) around a circuit.
The coloured bands denote the value in ohms.
1st band = first significant figure
2nd band = second significant figure
3rd band = number of noughts; i.e multiplier

Colour code:
0 black
1 brown
2 red
3 orange
4 yellow

5 green
6 blue
7 violet
8 grey
9 white

b) Potential
   Dividers

or

Uses all three tags of a variable resistance.
The voltage on the slider will vary
between the voltages at the two ends.

Fig. 4   Resistors

the flow of current. Do not try this, but a copper wire connected across a battery will cause a heavy current to flow, the wire
could heat up, and will quickly 'flatten the battery', that is,
lower its voltage. Obviously, the conductor is the medium
through which the electrons current can flow from the battery

and back into the battery. Generally, circuits have a more useful rôle to play than this!

Diodes (D1 . . .) – one-way controllers of electricity
A diode (Fig.5) is an electrical version of a one-way street. It is a two-terminal device that allows current to flow freely in one direction only, from anode (a) to cathode (k). The cathode end is usually marked with a band, a 'no-entry sign' for current.

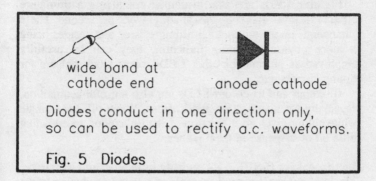

wide band at
cathode end

anode   cathode

Diodes conduct in one direction only,
so can be used to rectify a.c. waveforms.

Fig. 5   Diodes

Diodes can be used to rectify alternating currents, detect radio signals, to block direct currents and for isolation purposes.

Light-emitting diodes – visual indicators of electricity
Light-emitting diodes (Fig.6), known as LEDs, are useful components to have around when constructing projects. In

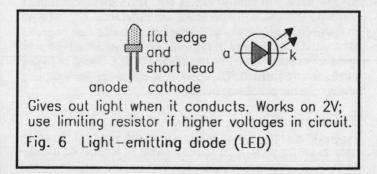

flat edge
and
short lead

anode   cathode

a   k

Gives out light when it conducts. Works on 2V;
use limiting resistor if higher voltages in circuit.

Fig. 6   Light–emitting diode (LED)

addition to the one-way current characteristic of normal diodes, LEDs emit light when a current flows through them. They are available in various shapes and sizes, in several colours (red, green, yellow or orange), and make excellent indicators. They must be connected the right way round in a circuit, and the maximum forward voltage (2V) and current (20mA) should not be exceeded. A limiting resistor is included in series when LEDs are connected to higher voltages.

Flashing LEDs are also available, containing a miniature circuit that gives on/off flashes at about twice per second. These can operate on 9V without a limiting resistor, and besides being a more obvious warning indicator, they can be usefully employed as pulsers for other LEDs, or as clock pulsers for timing circuits, etc.

Bi-colour and tri-colour LEDs are also a useful acquisition, especially for board game applications. When off, the opaque white colour gives no indication of its 'on' colour, so adds that little bit of suspense in team games.

Loudspeakers (LS1 . . .) – audible indicators of electricity
The loudspeaker is a good example of a sound-producing transducer, converting electrical energy into sound energy. Most work by electromagnetism. An audio signal applied to a voice coil, attached to a stiff cone, causes it to vibrate by the action of a powerful magnetic field to produce sound. Different sizes of loudspeakers are available, the larger the better if sound quality is important, especially to improve the bass frequencies. In this respect, it should be mounted on a baffle board otherwise the low notes will tend to cancel out. Try a speaker without a surround and you will appreciate the difference. For many of the projects, high fidelity is not the object, so the size of enclosure will dictate the size of the speaker. The voice coils of most speakers or either very low impedance (4 or 8 ohms) or higher impedance (64 ohms). To obtain best efficiency for a project, always use the stated impedance.

Transistors (TR1 . . .) – switchers of electricity
A transistor (Fig.7) is an active electronic device that can be used to switch signals, to amplify them, or to produce oscillations. It has three connections: the base (b), the emitter (e) and

the collector (c). There are two main types of transistors, npn and pnp. The npn type is much more common nowadays. Generally, the emitter is connected to the 0V line, and a small input current applied to the base is capable of producing much higher currents (often several hundred times larger) in the collector circuit.

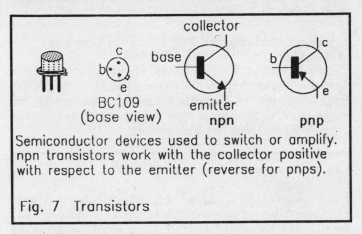

Semiconductor devices used to switch or amplify. npn transistors work with the collector positive with respect to the emitter (reverse for pnps).

Fig. 7   Transistors

Integrated circuits (IC1 . . .) – multi-switchers of electricity
Integrated circuits, or chips as they are called, consist of many transistors and other basic components on a single chip of silicon (Fig.8), wired as a complete circuit.

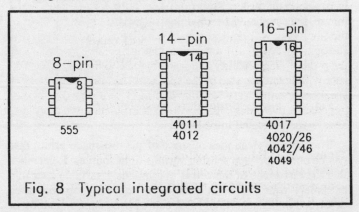

Fig. 8   Typical integrated circuits

For constructors, this has the advantage that many of the connections are already made, and complex circuits can be completed by the addition of a few extra components. Ten of the following projects incorporating integrated circuits would be far too complex on terminal blocks using discrete components (see also the author's *30 Simple IC Terminal Block Projects* (BP379)).

Light-dependent resistors (PCC1 ...) – sensing eyes of electricity

Cadmium sulphide is sensitive to visible light, and light-dependent resistors (LDRs) or photo-conductive cells (PCCs) made of this substance provide a useful means of sensing for the presence, or absence, of light. A typical LDR is shown in Figure 9 together with its circuit symbol.

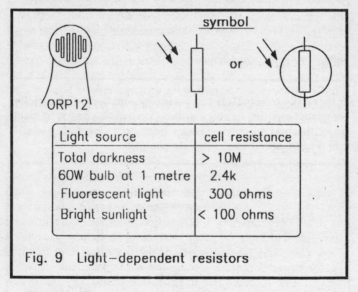

Light source	cell resistance
Total darkness	> 10M
60W bulb at 1 metre	2.4k
Fluorescent light	300 ohms
Bright sunlight	< 100 ohms

Fig. 9 Light–dependent resistors

The table gives an idea of some of the resistance values that can be obtained when sensing various light sources. Remember that the resistance of the cell is continuously variable over this extremely wide range; in addition to the more obvious uses described in Chapter 4, an LDR can be used experimentally in electronic musical circuits to control or vary pitch, loudness, vibrato, etc.

Connections

Although this book specifies terminal block connections, the experienced constructor will no doubt be able to work from the circuit diagrams and design printed circuits, etched or using stripboard, and 'solder on' regardless in traditional fashion. For the younger constructors, and less experienced, terminal blocks provide a simpler and safer solution for connections.

Terminal Blocks (TB1 . . .)
The moulded-plastic terminal blocks are readily available from the electrical accessory sections of DIY stores and are listed in mail-order catalogues. The 12-way, 2A strips are preferred, as the narrow spacing is better for components with short connecting leads. Where extra connections are required, the strips can easily be cut into shorter lengths with a junior hacksaw. In most cases, connection is easier if the strips are first mounted on a plywood or hardboard base to make the layout stable. Care should be taken to ensure that the terminal screws grip the bare ends of the components and connecting wires. This is especially necessary when two or more connections are to be made to the same terminal.

Awkward Components
A few of the components listed are not wire-ended, so it is necessary to attach short lengths of flexible wire to these when assembling the kit of parts. These awkward components include potentiometers, loudspeakers, transformers and some switches that have no screw terminals. With few exceptions these can easily be wire-wrapped as they often have terminal lugs with small holes to secure the wire connections. Ideally, these can be soldered and modification would only take a few minutes. In particular, the dual in-line holders for the integrated circuit need short leads soldering to them for connection to the terminal blocks. If you are not able or not permitted to solder these yourself, then ask a friend who is familiar with a soldering iron to make the connections for you. For the inte-

13

grated circuit projects, two terminal blocks are preferable, one on either side (see Fig. 35).

Wiring
Single plastic-covered copper wire is easier to use for links between the terminal blocks. Strip back the wire ends for about two centimetres so that screw terminal can grip the bare wire as mentioned. For longer connections, and those in constant use, multi-stranded covered wire offers more flexibility. To avoid short-circuits, especially when leads cross each other, plastic sleeving should be fitted over component lead-out wires such as resistor or transistor wire ends.

Tools
Few tools are needed for this type of project construction. The screwdriver blade for releasing and tightening the screws in the terminal blocks should match the slot in the screw-head; an oversize screwdriver, turned too vigorously, could easily strip the threads. The other basic tools are a pair of wire-strippers, and side-cutters to trim the component ends and connecting wires to size.

Circuits and Layouts

Before launching into the projects, it is worth noting that each includes both a circuit diagram and a practical layout diagram. Beginners will no doubt find the layout diagrams more useful, but would be well advised to compare them with the equivalent circuits to become more familiar with circuit conventions. In this way, students would quickly learn how to design their own circuits and transpose them from electronic graffiti to practical project layouts and vice versa. Those unfamiliar with reading circuit diagrams should refer to Project 1 for a basic introduction explaining how they are interpreted.

Chapter 3

CONTACT-OPERATED SENSORS

Numerous electronic systems use contacts as sensors, many of them associated with security systems. For instance, hidden contacts that trigger off alarm buzzers or switch on lights, when they sense the presence of an intruder.

Of course, there are many other uses for contact-operated sensors besides security. For example, in leisure and industry, totalising systems sometimes use the repetitive closing of a switch to count how many people have passed a turnstile, how many audience votes in a TV quiz show or to register that the correct number and denomination of coins are inserted in a vending machine.

In many cases, the contact is only the first step in the sensing chain. However, it sometimes controls some other function which may also be regarded as a sensing device. For instance, it could be used to switch a voltage, the value of which could be sensed by another circuit in the electronic system. So does this make it a contact sensor or a voltage sensor? It is difficult to put all sensing devices into neat categories. Obviously, there are some overlaps, but the projects in the various chapters cover a wide range of sensors and leave plenty of scope for the constructor to ring the changes. The sensors referred to in this chapter are touch-operated devices, although with the pressure-operated switches, 'touch' has a much wider meaning.

'Make' Contacts

Switches having contacts that close together, when operated, i.e. make contact, are referrred to as 'make' switches. Pushbutton switches and toggle switches, microswitches are the simplest contact switches to operate an electronic system. Connect a pushbutton switch in series with the supply voltage to a system and it works while you hold your finger on the button. If you want the system to work permanently, use a toggle switch instead of the pushbutton switch. In security systems, make switches for sensing intruders can be located strategically at likely points of entry, for instance, on doors or

15

windows. Alternatively, a make switch could be concealed under a door mat. Pressure mats incorporating several make contacts are commercially available for this purpose (see Pressure-operated switches, below).

'Break' Contacts

Sometimes an open contact is needed to operate a system. Switches that break contact when operated are called 'break' switches. This needs a little more thought, because electronic systems are not usually designed to operate when a contact is broken. The delayed latching alarm in Project 5 shows an application for sensing a break in a circuit. There are some obvious needs for break-contact sensors. Burglar alarms that operate when a wire is cut, or a window is broken by an intruder. Self-adhesive window foil is advertised by electronic component stockists specially for this purpose (Maplin order code YW50E). If the glass cracks, so does the foil, which indicates that break-contact sensors can offer a useful solution for break-ins.

Changeover Switches

Microswitches often have changeover contacts and can therefore serve as either a 'make' switch or a 'break' switch. However, in its changeover capacity, a changeover switch can be used as a sensing contact to switch over from some normal operation to an emergency or security situation, e.g. the changeover contacts could swap a courtesy light for an alarm buzzer.

Two-way Switching

A common application for two changeover switches is a two-way switching circuit where lights need to be controlled from different locations, e.g. the two ends of a corridor, or on a stairway. This can be done with two changeover switches as will be illustrated in the first project.

Pressure-operated Switches

The pressure mat, a rubber mat with several 'make' contacts, has already been mentioned, but some pressure-operated sensors depend upon the variation in resistance of a piece of

16

conductive foam, its resistance decreasing as it is compressed. Although both types of sensors are pressure-operated, they require different electronic processes (see Projects 28 and 29). Other pressure-operated sensors are activated by more natural elements than the size-ten boot of an intruder. Washing machines use a microswitch sensor activated by a diaphragm. A small tube from the drum housing carries water to the diaphragm which operates the microswitch at a certain pressure. This kind of pressure sensor will also respond to a flow of air in the tube, so could be used to control or indicate air pressure.

Some of the circuits illustrated in this book can be adapted for use with these or other sensors as you become familiar with the basic principles. Don't be afraid to experiment as you learn more about these projects.

Project 1 – Two-way Light Switch

This first project shows the beginner a simple method of transposing a circuit diagram into a practical layout. A simple two-way switching circuit is used to illustrate it.

Take a look at the circuit diagram of Figure 10. Note that the lines joining the component symbols represent the connecting wires and are usually drawn straight, and as short or long as convenient for the drawing. You will see that in the practical layout of Figure 11, they are often bent to take the shortest route. Terminals have been superimposed on the circuit diagram of Figure 10 to correspond with those on the layout diagram of Figure 11. Notice that a terminal pair inevitably occurs between two components. This is a fairly good indication of how many terminal blocks are required to lay out a circuit. In this example, two extra blocks were needed because the two changeover switches were located at a distance from each other. Sometimes extra blocks are needed when components have short wire ends, or if there are several connections to the same point in a circuit.

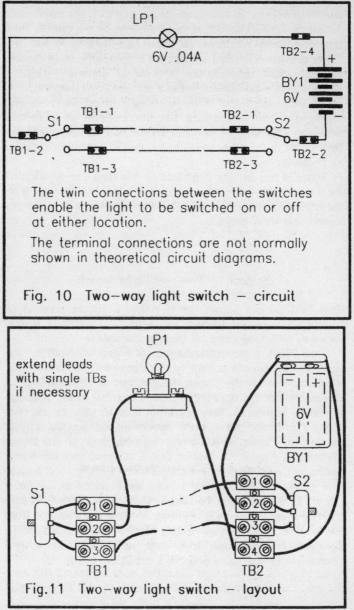

The twin connections between the switches enable the light to be switched on or off at either location.

The terminal connections are not normally shown in theoretical circuit diagrams.

Fig. 10 Two-way light switch — circuit

extend leads with single TBs if necessary

Fig.11 Two-way light switch — layout

Circuit (Fig.10)

When the two changeover switches S1and S2 are in opposite positions the negative end of battery BY1 is disconnected from the lamp LP1. However, as shown, when either S1 or S2 is switched over, a series circuit is completed from the positive (+) end of the battery, through the lamp and via S1 and S2 back to the negative (−) end of the battery, to light the lamp. Note that the twin connections between the outer poles of the switches alternatively complete the circuit, depending on which switch is used.

Layout (Fig.11)

The two terminal blocks, TB1 (3-way) and TB2 (4-way), provide a compact layout for this simple circuit.

Components for Project 1

Lamp
LP1   6V 0.04A MES bulb

Switches
S1, S2   changeover (2 off)

Terminal Blocks
TB1   3-way
TB2   4-way

Miscellaneous
6V battery and connections, plastic-insulated wire.

Project 2 – Fisherman's Bite Alarm

You are sitting on the bank of a river at dusk when there's a gentle tug on your line to remind you that the fish are still biting. The problem is that you have dozed off, or been distracted, and blissfully unaware that you are about to lose your bait and your prospective supper along with it. Fortunately, disappointments like this, and stories of the one that got away, can be avoided if you make up this fisherman's bite alarm, a simple series circuit with light and sound indicators. For those not keen on fishing, the circuit could be used as a simple make-operated alarm for other purposes.

Circuit (Fig.12)

This is an example of a simple circuit, showing four components connected in series across a 9-volt battery. The small current through the circuit is sufficient to bring on the light-emitting diode (LED) and sound the buzzer just in case you are dozing.

When the line is tugged, current flows from the positive pole of the battery through switch S1, the miniature buzzer WD1, the current-limiting resistor R1 and the light-emitting diode (LED) D1 to the negative pole of the battery. The lever of the low-torque microswitch S1 attached to the line, closes at the slightest tug.

Beginners should note that early scientists thought that current flows from positive to negative, as stated above. It was later discovered that the movement of electrons was from negative to positive. There were probably some red faces at the time, but the convention remains that current flows from positive to negative. On the few occasions when it is important to make a clear distinction, we refer either to *conventional current flow* or *electron flow*.

Layout (Fig.13)

As the layout needs to be on the rod, it needs to be small. Fortunately, none of the components occupies much space, and all could be suitably mounted on a small strip of plywood.

It is important to make sure that the buzzer and the LED are connected the right way round. The positive lead of the buzzer, usually indicated red, should be towards the positive of the circuit; the cathode (k) of the LED, usually denoted by a flat on its base, should be nearest to the 0V rail.

Components for Project 2

Resistor
R1   470 ohms

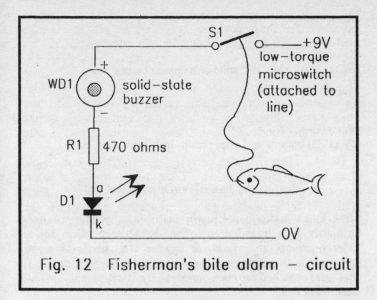

Fig. 12 Fisherman's bite alarm — circuit

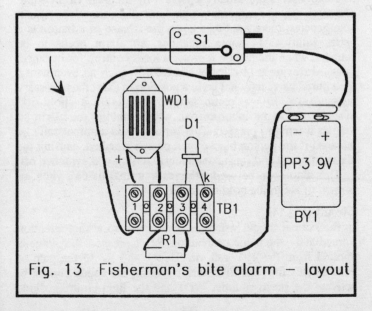

Fig. 13 Fisherman's bite alarm — layout

Semiconductor
D1   LED

Sounder
WD1   6V solid-state piezo buzzer

Switch
S1   low-torque microswitch

Miscellaneous
9V (PP3) battery and clip, plastic-insulated wire, etc.

Project 3 – Panic Switch with Hold-off

Here is an audio/visual alarm that has a number of uses. Primarily it is intended as a hand-held panic alarm for an elderly person, an invalid, or anyone who needs to attract attention in an emergency. It incorporates a latching device so that once switched on, even momentarily, it will remain on until eventually reset.

Panic alarms are usually activated by the push of a button. Although this is convenient to get immediate attention in most emergencies, there are times when the release of a button is a better solution. In some situations, an alarm needs to be sounded when the person it protects loses control, for instance, faints, dozes or is physically attacked. In such an eventuality, the injured party may not be in a position to exert the necessary pressure to 'hit' a panic button. However, a 'hold-off' pushbutton can be incorporated, which inhibits the alarm so long as it remains pressed. This button would automatically be released if the person blacked-out or was attacked, causing the alarm to sound and flash continuously until it was switched off.

This alarm can be used either as a normal panic switch, or primed to act in the hold-off facility.

Circuit (Fig.14)
In the normal mode, where the user needs to attract attention immediately, the panic pushbutton, S1, is pressed. A voltage is applied from the +9V rail via S1, R1 and R2 to the gate of THY1. This fires the thyristor, triggering the anode current to activate the piezo sounder WD1 and the light-emitting diode

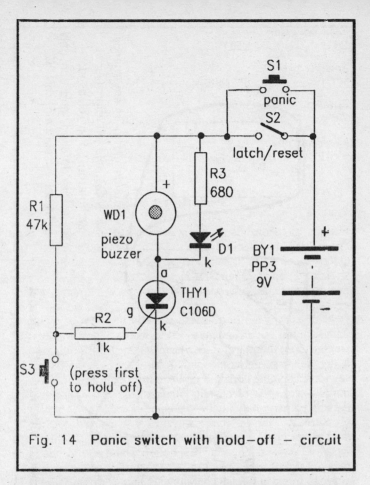

Fig. 14 Panic switch with hold—off — circuit

D1. This alarm condition continues until the panic button S1 is released.

Alternatively, where the user realises that a potentially dangerous situation is developing, the circuit can be primed in the hold-off (standby) mode. The hold-off pushbutton S3 is first pressed and held in, and S2 is switched to the latched position, while still holding in S3. The contacts of S3 short-circuit the gate voltage (to the 0V line), normally applied to the thyristor, preventing it from conducting. In an emergency, if S3 is

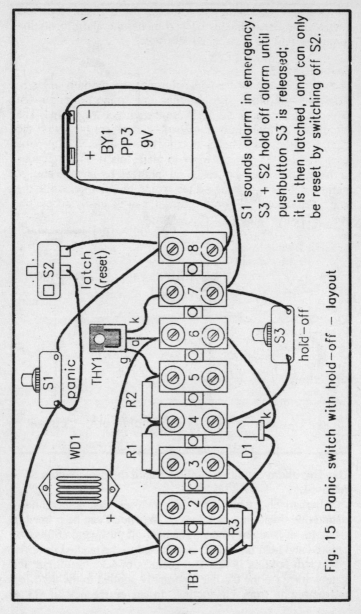

S1 sounds alarm in emergency. S3 + S2 hold off alarm until pushbutton S3 is released; it is then latched, and can only be reset by switching off S2.

Fig. 15 Panic switch with hold-off — layout

24

released the gate voltage is restored, the thyristor fires and operates the alarm. In this latched mode, the alarm condition continues until S2 is switched off (reset).

Layout (Fig.15)

The circuit layout for the panic alarm fits easily on a single 8-way terminal block. Ensure that the connections for the thyristor, the sounder and LED are the correct way round. The layout can be fitted into a small plastic project box, with the LED, sounder, and switches suitably mounted. As S2 is also the reset switch, it is perhaps wiser to make this less conspicuous so that the alarm cannot easily be inhibited by anyone else. A miniature unmarked slide switch would be suitable, while the panic pushbutton S1, wired across it, can be easily accessible and clearly marked.

Components for Project 3

Resistors

R1	47k
R2	1k
R3	680

Semiconductors

D1	LED
THY1	C106D thyristor

Switches

S1	push-to-make, non-locking (panic)
S2	miniature SPST (latch/reset)
S3	push-to-make, non-locking (hold-off)

Sounder

WD1	piezo buzzer

Terminal block

TB1	8-way

Miscellaneous

9V (PP3) battery with clip, small plastic project box, plastic-insulated connecting wire, etc.

Project 4 – Two-way Decision-maker

'Whose turn is it?' is a familiar question when playing board games, particularly if they drag on a bit, or turns are subject to interruptions. Here's a simple circuit with two LEDs, two changeover switches and an on/off switch, that will indicate the state of play however long the game lasts, and ensures that turns are taken in strict rotation.

The circuit senses the state of the two changeover switches, which perform a 2-input AND-gate function to bring on one of the LEDs depending on the switching combination.

Circuit (Fig.16)

The circuit is similar to the two-way lighting circuit of Figure 10, except in this case the lights have been duplicated and inserted in the two arms linking the changeover switches. With the circuit switched on (S3), no current will flow in the circuit as drawn and therefore neither LED will glow. This particular state of the switches S1 and S2 actually means that the 'green' player has finished and the 'red' player's turn is due to start. Operating the 'start' changeover switch S1 will confirm this. Current will flow from the positive side of battery BY1 via S1, through the D1 arm, S2 and the limiting resistor R1 to the negative side of BY1. The red LED D1 glows to indicate the 'red' player's turn. After the turn is completed, the 'finish' switch S2 is operated to turn off D1. When 'start' switch S1 is next operated, current will flow through the D2 arm, i.e. LED D2 will light to indicate the 'green' player's turn. At the conclusion, D2 is switched off by the S2 contact, which again sets up the cathode end connection for the D1 arm.

The on/off switch S3 would appear to be superfluous, but does serve a useful purpose. If play is suspended during a player's turn, S3 can be switched off, without disturbing the switching sequence. At switch-on, the appropriate LED will be restored to indicate who is in play.

Layout (Fig.17)

The layout can be mounted on an 8-way terminal block. The changeover switches will each need to have three flexible wires attached so that they can be connected to the terminal block. A

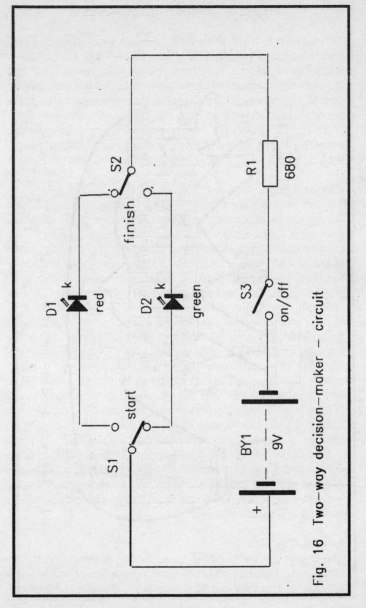

Fig. 16 Two—way decision—maker — circuit

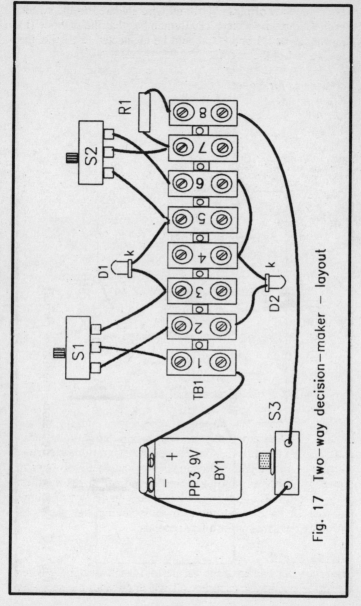

Fig. 17 Two-way decision-maker – layout

28

few centimetres of plastic-covered wire soldered to the switch terminals should do the trick. Remember that the cathode (k) connections of D1 and D2 should be connected to S2, i.e. the negative end of the circuit.

Components for Project 4

Resistor
R1   680Ω

Semiconductors
D1   LED (red)
D2   LED (green)

Switches
S1, S2   changeover (2 off)
S3   SPST

Terminal block
TB1   8-way

Miscellaneous
9V battery (PP3) and clip, plastic-insulated wire.

Project 5 – Delayed Latching Alarm

When is an alarm not an alarm? Very often, judging by the number of times a day that we hear a familiar warning bleep and discover it is just another false alarm. Unfortunately, most alarm systems, unlike watchdogs, are unable to distinguish between owners and intruders and sound off at the slightest provocation. This alarm circuit has a built-in delay that allows the user quick exit or entrance after setting the alarm by inhibiting the sensing for a few seconds.

Circuit (Fig.18)
The sensor for this circuit is the push-to-break switch S2, wired across the electrolytic capacitor C1 which provides the necessary

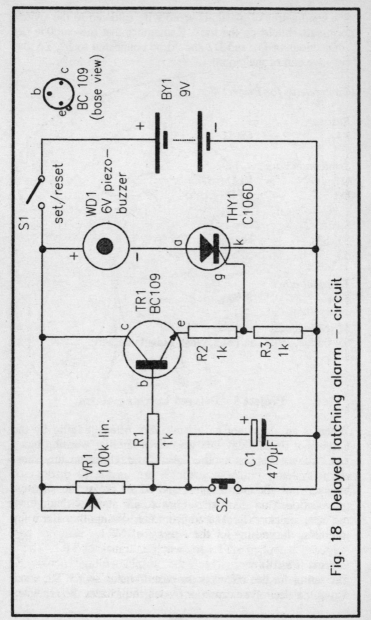

Fig. 18 Delayed latching alarm — circuit

30

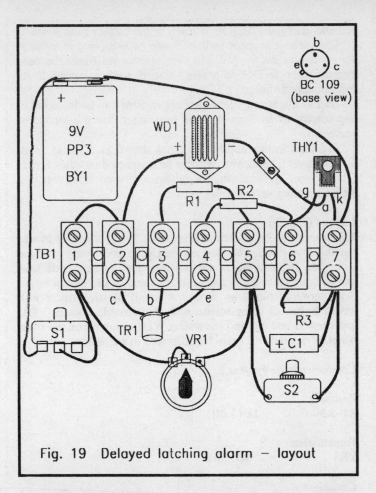

Fig. 19 Delayed latching alarm — layout

delay. When the switch contacts of S2 are broken, for example when a door or window is opened, C1 starts to charge via variable resistor VR1 and S1 from the 9V supply. After a few seconds, depending on the setting of VR1, sufficient base current is supplied via R1 to switch on transistor TR1. This is an emitter-follower stage, the output voltage across R3 providing the gate voltage to fire the thyristor THY1. The anode (a) to cathode (k) current activates the buzzer WD1, which remains energised until S1 is reset, or the battery runs down.

The variable resistor and/or C1 can be increased in value if longer delays are needed. The base resistor R1 limits the base current through TR1 to a safe value if VR1 is turned to its minimum resistance.

An LED in series with a limiting resistor can be included in the output, as in Project 3, or substituted for the buzzer if preferred.

Although in this application S2 is shown as a single break switch, several break switches can be connected in series across C1 for other applications, for example, if used as an intruder alarm covering several entry points.

Layout (Fig.19)

The circuit can be accommodated on a 7-way terminal block, but the thyristor leads may not easily be connected to three terminals. If soldering is not possible, the central anode lead can be coupled to the negative (black) lead of the buzzer by an extra terminal block as shown. A small plastic project box would house all components, with the variable resistor VR1, switches S1 and S2, and the buzzer WD1 mounted on the front panel. If desired, VR1 can be calibrated in seconds.

Components for Project 5

Resistors
R1–R3   1k (3 off)

Potentiometer
VR1   100k lin

Capacitor
C1   470µ 10V elect.

Semiconductors
TR1   BC109 transistor
THY1   C106D thyristor

Sounder
WD1   6V piezo buzzer

Switches

S1	SPST (on/off)
S2	push-to-break, non-locking (see text)

Miscellaneous
9V battery (PP3) with clip, plastic project box, plastic-insulated wire, etc.

Chapter 4

LIGHT-OPERATED SENSORS

Devices that detect the presence, or absence, of light and produce resultant electrical effects have a number of useful applications in home and industry. For example, lights that automatically switch on when the sun sets, and switch off at sunrise; alarms that sound when a sensor is activated by an intruder's torch, or when a beam of light is interrupted. Light-operated sensors can also serve to bring on courtesy lights on poorly lit pathways, or to illuminate entrances on the approach of a caller.

Besides the domestic applications, there are many uses for light-operated sensing devices for counting and measuring in commerce and industry. An interrupted light beam can be sensed to count revolutions of a shaft, or the number of articles on an assembly line. Sometimes the degree of light needs to be measured, as in the case of a photographic light meter for checking or controlling camera settings. Photoelectric devices used as sensors are listed as follows:

Light-dependent Resistors (LDRs)
A light-sensitive resistor widely-used for visible light sensing is the ORP 12, a cadmium sulphide photo-conductive cell with a spectral response that broadly follows that of the human eye. Its resistance falls logarithmically as the light intensity increases. Typically, its resistance falls from over $10M\Omega$ in total darkness to less than 150Ω in sunlight.

Photodiodes and Phototransistors
Reverse-biased p-n silicon junctions are inherently photo-sensitive and can be made to respond to either visible or infra-red (IR) light. The junctions of normal diodes and transistors are covered with opaque material to avoid this effect, but the photo-effect can be exploited by using translucent material. Like the LDR, the junction acts as a high impedance in the dark and low impedance in the light. The photodiode is

far less sensitive than the LDR, but responds more quickly to changes in light levels.

Optocouplers
As the name implies, an optocoupler is a device for coupling two circuits, so that one can be used to control the other. However, the major feature is that both circuits are fully isolated and it can be used to couple either analogue or digital circuits.

Basically, an optocoupler houses a light-emitting diode (LED) as input, usually an IR (infrared) type, and a photodiode or phototransistor as output.

Photovoltaic Cell
Semiconductor materials such as selenium generate a voltage depending on the amount of light that falls on their surface. These cells are used as sensors in light meters and on a larger scale for solar generator systems to power satellites, telephone repeater stations and lighting applications in remote areas.

Project 6 – Simple Beam-breaker Detector

This detector circuit is activated when a beam of light directed on to a light-depending resistor is interrupted. An alarm is sounded and remains on until the circuit is manually reset. The light source and the sensor can be located on opposite sides of a path or corridor, for instance, at a point of entry.

Circuit (Fig.20)
The light-dependent resistor PCC1 is part of a potential divider that includes VR1, R1, across the supply rails. The voltage applied to the gate of THY1 is adjusted by VR1 to hold off the thyristor when the light beam is illuminating PCC1. When the beam is interrupted, the resistance of PCC1 increases, thus causing the voltage on the gate to increase and fire the thyristor. The resultant current between anode and cathode energises the alarm WD1, which continues to sound even if the light beam is restored. The circuit can be reset by switching S1 off momentarily.

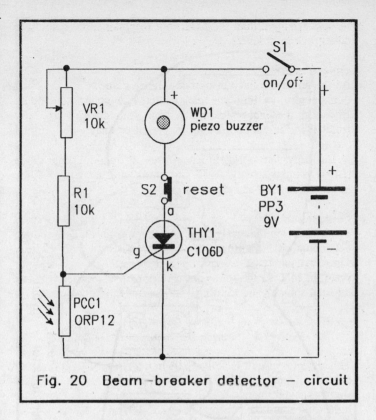

Fig. 20 Beam-breaker detector — circuit

If a visual alarm is preferred, WD1 can be replaced by a light-emitting diode with a limiting resistor of 680 ohms in series.

Layout (Fig.21)

A 7-way terminal block is more than adequate to make up this circuit. Make sure that the piezo sounder and the thyristor connections are correctly wired. A torch should be adequate for a beam of several metres, especially if the light-dependent resistor is made directional by mounting it at the end of a long tube so that the ambient light is screened from it. This can be a cardboard or plastic tube about the same diameter as the LDR,

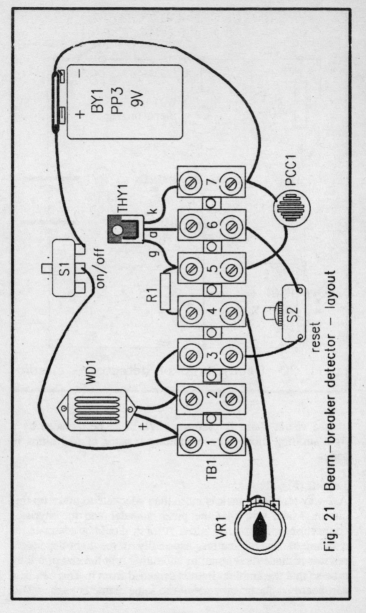

Fig. 21 Beam–breaker detector — layout

and at least 3 metres long. To improve the screening, the inner surface should be painted matt black.

For some applications the torch and tube are not necessary, for instance where the sensor is required to operate when daylight fades or when a room light is put out.

Components for Project 6

Resistor
R1   10k

Potentiometer
VR1   10k (linear)

Semiconductors
THY1   thyristor C106D
PCC1   light-dependent resistor ORP12

Sounder
WD1   6V piezo buzzer

Switches
S1   SPST (on/off)
S2   push-to-break or SPST (reset)

Terminal block
TB1   7-way

Miscellaneous
9V battery (PP3) and clip, light source (torch), plastic-insulated wire links, etc.

Project 7 – Smoke Alarm

Smoke alarm detectors generally fall into two categories: either relying on the fact that air laden with smoke reflects light, or that at the same time it obstructs light. Basically, it means that when using the reflective principle, light reflected by the smoke

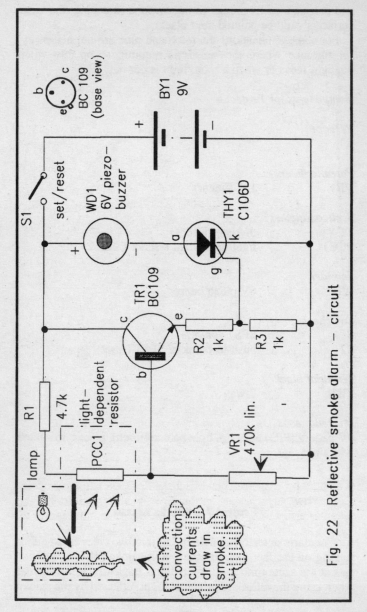

Fig. 22 Reflective smoke alarm – circuit

40

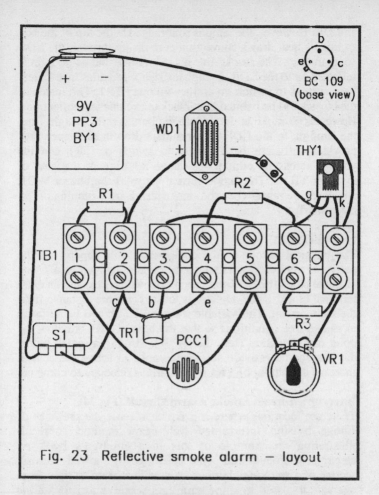

Fig. 23 Reflective smoke alarm — layout

is sensed by a light-dependent resistor (LDR) to operate an alarm; however, when using the direct-beam principle, a light beam, interrupted by the smoke, is excluded from the sensor to operate an alarm.

Reflective Smoke Alarm Circuit (Fig.22)
Reflective-type smoke detectors are designed so that a barrier in a light-tight box prevents the rays of a lamp being 'seen' by

an LDR. However, the lamp is so arranged at the top of the box so that its heat draws convection currents up through the LDR compartment. The smoke-free air is invisible and as no light is reflected on to the LDR, its high resistance provides insufficient base current to switch on emitter-follower TR1. The inside of the box should be painted matt black to exclude any reflections. However, if smoke is drawn into the box, it reflects light from the lamp on to the LDR. The resultant drop in resistance now provides sufficient base current to switch on TR1 and the voltage across its emitter resistance R3 triggers the gate of thyristor THY1. The anode current activates the buzzer WD1, which can be reset, when the smoke clears, by switching off S1 momentarily.

Layout (Fig.23)

The physical layout of the components will depend on the particular application. Although the circuit is shown on a 7-way terminal block the LDR may need extension wires, and an extra terminal block, if the detector is located at some distance from the main circuit. The variable resistor VR1 should be adjusted in smoke-free conditions so that the base of TR1 is below the point of conduction (less than 0.7V). Striking a match below the box should provide sufficient smoke to active the sensor. Increase the setting of VR1 if the alarm is reluctant to come on.

Interrupted-beam Smoke Alarm Circuit (Fig.24)

There are locations where it is easier to sense the presence of smoke by the interrupted light-beam method. I recall illustrating an example of this in a children's book on electronics, co-authored some years ago. It showed a cross-section of a smoking chimney stack with a beam of light from one side focussed to shine on a light-sensitive resistor on the opposite side.

The control circuit for the light-beam detector must of course be opposite to that of the reflective method. This is easily arranged by reversing the circuit positions of PCC1 and VR1. In this case, the light-beam normally shines on PCC1, and its reduced resistance holds off TR1 (base-emitter less than 0.7V). However, when the light-beam is interrupted, the resistance of the light-dependent resistor increases and the

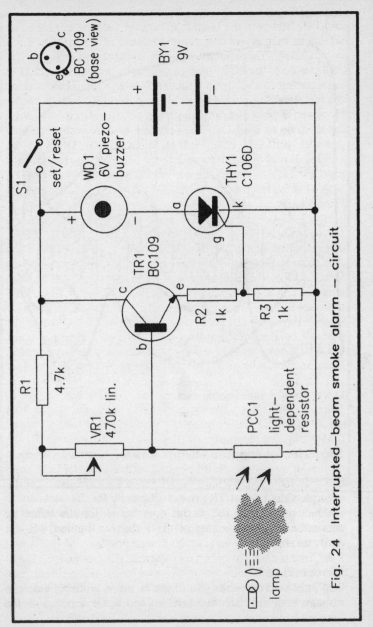

Fig. 24 Interrupted-beam smoke alarm — circuit

43

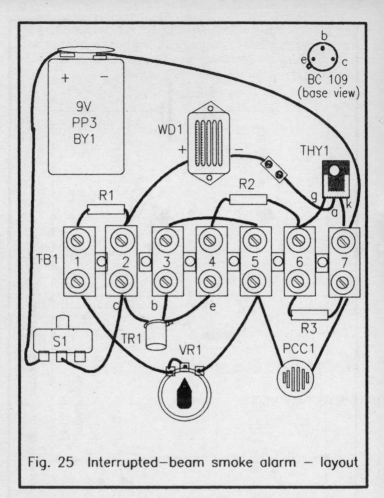

Fig. 25 Interrupted—beam smoke alarm — layout

voltage at the base of TR1 rises sufficiently for the transistor to conduct. After that, the circuit operates as for the reflective version. The emitter voltage of TR1 triggers the thyristor and activates the alarm.

Layout (Fig.25)

The light-beam detector part of the layout is probably easier to arrange than the reflective version, and again depends on the

44

type of application. A lens arrangement may be necessary in some cases to concentrate the light beam. Otherwise, apart from reversing the positions of PCC1 and VR1, the terminal block layout remains the same as Figure 23.

Components for Project 7

Resistors
R1   4.7k
R2, R3   1k (2 off)

Potentiometer
VR1   470k lin.

Semiconductors
PCC1   ORP12 light-dependent resistor
THY1   C106D thyristor
TR1   BC109

Sounder
WD1   6V piezo buzzer

Switch
S1   SPST (on/off)

Terminal Block
TB1   7-way

Miscellaneous
9V battery (PP3) with clip.

Project 8 – Light-operated Relay

In this project, a relay is used as a transducer to show how it offers more flexibility at the output of a circuit. Magnetic and electromagnetic sensors are described in more detail in Chapter 7.

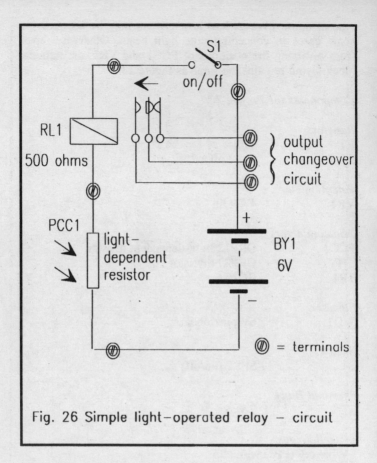

Fig. 26 Simple light—operated relay — circuit

A relay can be used to isolate circuits, to operate several other circuits, or to drive heavier loads such as higher wattage lights or motors.

The simplest light-operated relay circuit, shown in Figure 26, can be constructed using only two components, a relay and a light-dependent resistor connected in series across a battery. With the LDR at about 2 metres from a 100W lamp the circuit current was about 1mA and the relay was inoperative. As the LDR was brought nearer to the lamp the current rose gradually to 10mA, at which level the relay operated.

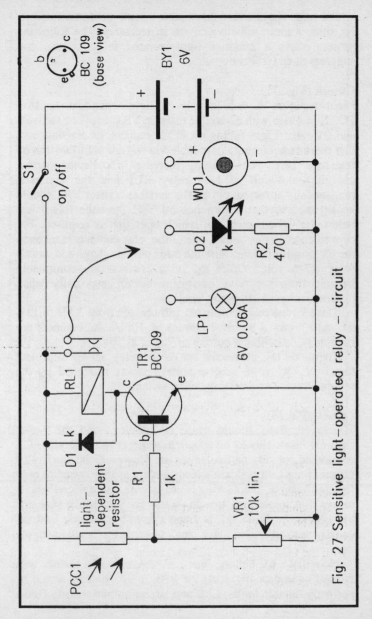

Fig. 27 Sensitive light–operated relay – circuit

For some applications this simple circuit would be suitable, but often a more sensitive circuit is necessary. The following project offers a sensitive light-operated relay circuit, and suggests three typical outputs.

Circuit (Fig.27)

Light-detection is achieved by a light-dependent resistor, PCC1, in series with a variable resistor, VR1, between the +6V and 0V rails. Light falling on PCC1 reduces its resistance so that more base current is available via resistor R1 to switch on transistor TR1. The resulting increase in collector current energises the coil of reed relay RL1 and the contacts, magnetically attracted, close. The variable resistor VR1 should be adjusted so that it switches off TR1 (and the relay) just below the light intensity at which operation is required. For convenience, in this circuit, one of the relay contacts is taken to the 6V positive rail, because the three outputs suggested can all work off 6 volts. Often the relay contacts are completely isolated from the relay energising circuit, especially when different voltages are being handled.

The 5V reed relay coil listed will operate from 3.8V to 11V d.c. and draws a nominal current of 10mA. Its contacts are capable of switching a current of 1 amp at 10V.

The diode D1, connected across the relay, serves to protect transistor TR1 from reverse voltage spikes produced by the self-inductance of the relay coil at switch-off.

Layout (Fig.28)

The layout itself should cause no problem, and the 7-way terminal block should be adequate, especially if the circuit is earmarked for one particular sensor. However, the reed relay pins will need short flexible leads adding as they measure only four millimetres. If soldering is not for you, ask a friend who is handy with a soldering iron to do this for you. Make sure that the protective diode D1 is fitted correctly; cathode end (k) usually marked with a black band, towards the positive supply rail.

Note that a 6V battery, four 1.5V AA cells in a battery box, is used instead of the usual 9V PP3. A PP3 battery would be perfectly suitable for the LED and buzzer outputs, taking 10mA

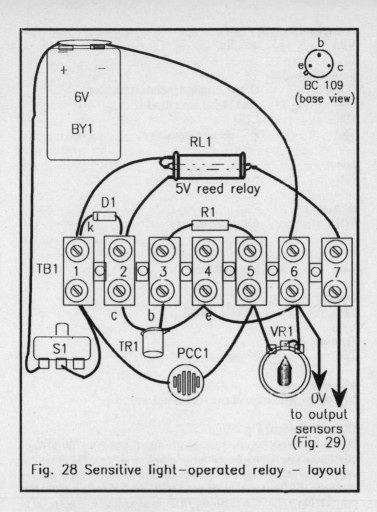

Fig. 28 Sensitive light—operated relay — layout

or so, but if a lamp output is required, this will demand more power (e.g. 60mA at 6V) and will reduce the life of the battery.

Components for Project 8

Resistor
R1   1k
R2   470Ω

49

Potentiometer
VR1   10k lin.

Semiconductors
PCC1   ORP12 light-dependent resistor
D1   1N4148 silicon diode
D2   LED
TR1   BC109 npn transistor

Lamp
LP1   6V 0.06A MES bulb

Sounder
WD1   6V piezo buzzer

Relay
RL1   5V reed relay

Switch
S1   SPST (on/off)

Terminal Block
TB1   7-way

Miscellaneous
6V battery with clip, plastic-insulated wire.

Output sensors (Fig.29)
If you are likely to use a range of output sensors with this, or other projects, it may be useful to make up a few of your choice on a terminal block. The three shown in this figure have a common 0V line, so can be used with the 6V output from this project. Note that if a flashing LED is used, there is no need to fit the series resistor R2 shown in Figure 27.

More sensors can be added if the terminal block is extended.

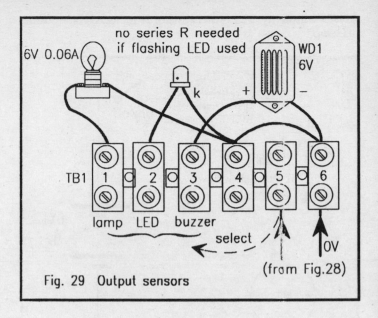

Fig. 29 Output sensors

Project 9 – Simple Light Meter

The fact that the resistance of a light-dependent resistor falls when the light intensity on it increases suggests an ideal method of measuring visible light. Measure the resistance, and you measure the light level. There are more sensitive circuits than the simple series circuit used in this project, but the basic principles are the same. In this circuit a meter in series with the light-dependent resistor measures the current supplied by a battery, which varies according to the resistance of the LDR. A circuit using a phototransistor would give greater sensitivity.

Circuit (Fig.30)
This light meter follows a logarithmic law, and a suitable scale can be made by comparing results with an accurate light meter. It consists of a series circuit: meter M1, the LDR PCC1 and a preset variable resistor VR1 across a battery. The meter M1 has a full-scale deflection of 250µA, but a 100µA meter would give

51

greater sensitivity. The preset resistor is included for adjusting the zero.

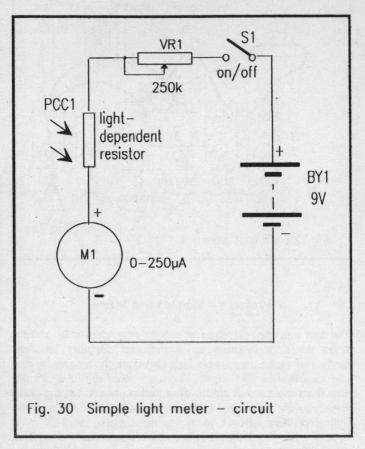

Fig. 30 Simple light meter – circuit

Layout (Fig.31)
The layout poses no problems, but remember that the meter must be connected with negative (–) terminal to the black (–) lead of the battery clip. If preferred, a 3V battery (2 × 1.5V AA cells in a battery box) can be used instead of a PP3 battery.

The meter, switch and preset resistor can be mounted on the front panel of a small plastic project box.

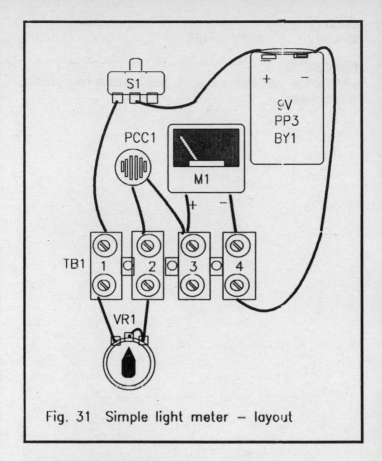

Fig. 31 Simple light meter – layout

Components for Project 9

Potentiometer
VR1   250k preset

Meter
M1   250μA f.s.d. (see text)

Semiconductor
PCC1   ORP12

Switch

S1   SPST (on/off)

Miscellaneous

6–9V battery and clip (see text), small project box, plastic-insulated wire.

Chapter 5

HEAT-OPERATED SENSORS

Our fingertips, elbows and toes are often pressed into service as sensors to find out whether objects are hot or cold, and our tongues get burnt occasionally if we are not careful, all in the cause of heat-sensing. However, we sometimes need a more precise measurement of temperature, or one that indicates and reacts to a particular change of temperature, perhaps in our absence. The measureing side can be satisfied by the humble liquid-filled thermometer, but if we need the measurement to perform some other function, for example, to record a value, sound an alarm, switch off a heater, close a valve, or a window, etc., it is easier to use an electronic heat-operated sensor, processed by a suitable system.

There are several heat sensors that can be used, their suitability depending on the application.

Thermostats

These temperature devices are familiar domestically as controllers for room heating systems, ovens, water heaters, and irons, for example. They mostly consist of a bimetal strip, two metals of different thermal coefficients of expansion being mechanically joined to form the strip. As the temperature changes, the two metal parts vary in length. As a result, the strip bends into a curved shape, which closes two contacts. In many devices, the temperature of switchover is adjustable over a given temperature range. In effect this is another contact-operated sensor and could be used with one of the circuit projects of Chapter 3.

Thermistors

In electronics, thermistors are widely used for temperature sensing as their resistance varies directly with changes in temperature. They are semiconductor devices, often made from sintered mixtures of sulphides or oxides of metals. For most temperature measuring applications, thermistors are used that have a negative temperature coefficient (NTC), i.e. the

55

resistance falls as the temperature increases. Thermistors were fitted in series with the valve and tube heaters in television sets, to counteract the initial surge current at switch-on when the heaters were cold. The particular thermistor used in the following projects has a nominal resistance of 27kΩ (twenty-seven thousand ohms) at 0 deg. C. Others are available in rod, bead or disc types, with various values suitable for temperature ranges between –50 and +300 deg. C.

Silicon Diodes

The forward voltage drop of silicon diodes (typically about 600mV) is temperature-dependent, so these can be used as heat sensors. With constant current flowing, for every increase in temperature of 1 deg. C, this forward voltage drops by about 2mV.

Thermocouples

If two dissimilar metal conductors are joined, and if two such junctions appearing in a circuit are subjected to different temperatures, a small potential difference can be detected across the pair of junctions. This is known as the Seebeck or thermoelectric effect. The junctions can be made by twisting the wires together, better still by soldering them. The size of the voltage depends on the difference in temperature between the sensing junction and the cold, or reference, junction. Thermocouples are generally used for measuring over wide temperature ranges. Greater voltages can be obtained by using a thermopile, i.e. several thermocouples connected in series. In this case, the junctions must be in two groups: the reference junctions, and the sensing junctions. Constantan and iron wires are often used in commercial thermocouples, but a do-it-yourself device can be made by soldering a piece of copper wire between two pieces of wire cut from a paper clip. This primitive thermocouple should generate about a millivolt depending on the heat applied to the sensing junction.

Platinum Resistance Detector

A thermometer using a platinum coil or film on a ceramic former, is based on the fact that the resistance of a metallic conductor increases as its temperature rises. Such a thermometer can be used over a wide range, but the coil is rather bulky because of the length of wire necessary. Its low resistance can also be a problem when connecting into a measuring bridge.

Project 10 – Simple Ice Indicator

Basically, this circuit uses a thermistor to sense when icy conditions are present and gives a visual warning. However, as a variable control is used to adjust the circuit to operate at freezing point, there is no reason why the control should not be calibrated to indicate other setpoints on the temperature scale. Although not particularly accurate, there are a number of applications where this circuit could be useful. If desired, the flashing LED could be replaced by a piezo buzzer, or a standard LED in series with a 680Ω resistor.

Circuit (Fig.32)

The thermistor TH1 forms a potential divider with variable resistor VR1 across the 9V supply rail. At higher temperatures than freezing point the resistance of TH1 is progressively less than 27k, e.g. 10k at 25 deg. C and 1k at 100 deg. C. Above freezing, the variable resistor VR1 is adjusted so that the base current to TR1 via R1 is not sufficient for the transistor to conduct. Consequently, the flashing LED, D1, is not activated. However, as the temperature drops to zero, the resistance of TH1 increases (to 27k) and the voltage across it increases causing TR1 to conduct and bring on the flashing LED, D1.

The thermistor TH1 must, of course, be located at the sensing point. Immerse the thermistor in iced water to adjust VR1 to the point at which the LED flashes. Make sure that the connections to the thermistor are well insulated otherwise you will get a false reading. Moisture across the leads would reduce the resistance and tend to hold off the transistor, and therefore the alarm.

If you are looking for a simple high temperature alarm circuit, reverse the positions of VR1 and TH1.

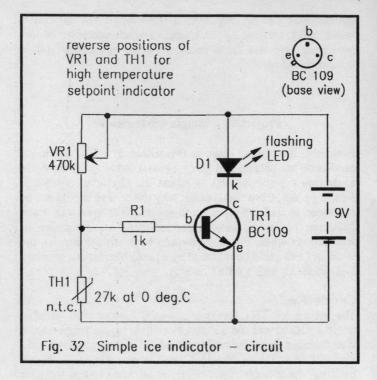

Fig. 32 Simple ice indicator — circuit

Layout (Fig.33)

Although this circuit fits comfortably on a 6-way terminal block, it may be necessary to use an extra 2-way block and a length of twin flex if the thermistor is required to do its sensing at some remote location – in the garage, out in the garden, or at the edge of the fishpond. Note that the flashing LED must be connected correctly. It includes a tiny circuit enabling it to flash at once or twice per second to attract attention, and needs no limiting resistor. A standard LED in series with a 680Ω resistor can be substituted if a flashing LED is not available.

Components for Project 10

Resistor
R1　　　　　1k

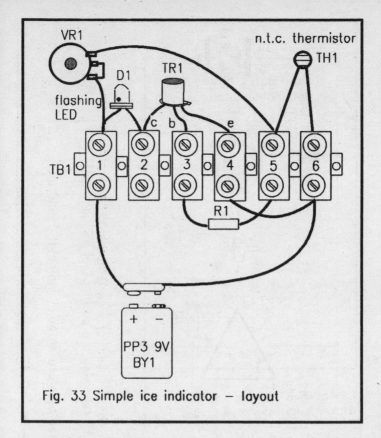

Fig. 33 Simple ice indicator — layout

Potentiometer
VR1   470k lin.

Semiconductors
TR1   BC109
D1   flashing LED
TH1   thermistor (n.t.c.) 27k at 0 deg. C

Miscellaneous
9V battery (PP3) and clip, small project box, plastic-insulated wire.

59

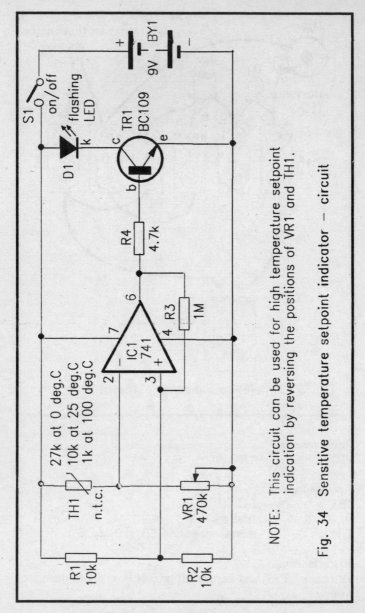

NOTE: This circuit can be used for high temperature setpoint indication by reversing the positions of VR1 and TH1.

Fig. 34 Sensitive temperature setpoint indicator – circuit

60

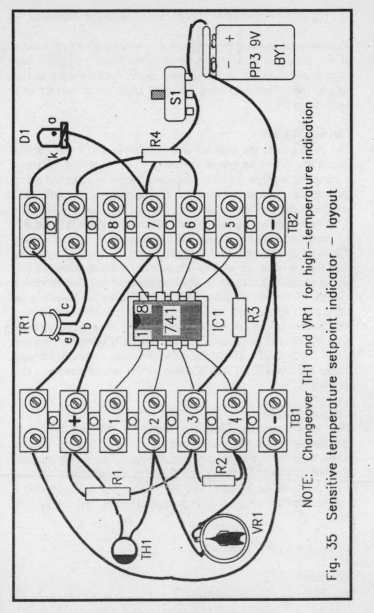

NOTE: Changeover TH1 and VR1 for high–temperature indication

Fig. 35 Sensitive temperature setpoint indicator – layout

61

Project 11 – Sensitive Temperature Setpoint Indicator

This temperature setpoint indicator is a more sensitive version of the previous circuit. It uses an operational amplifier as a comparator to ensure a cleaner switchover for the output alarm. Again, the output can be a standard LED, piezo buzzer or a relay, if preferred.

Circuit (Fig.34)

The output from the thermal sensor is applied to a comparator circuit that drives an output transistor stage. As stated, by using a comparator stage a faster snap-over action is achieved when the setpoint voltage is exceeded. The operational amplifier IC1 compares the voltage at the junction of TH1 and VR1 with a 4.5V reference at the junction of potential divider R1 and R2. At zero temperature, when TH1 resistance is approximately 27k, VR1 is adjusted so that input 2 of IC1 falls slightly lower than that on input 3 (+4.5V). This causes the output on pin 6 to swing positive, aided by a small amount of positive feedback via R3. The resulting base current applied by R4 switches on transistor TR1 and activates the flashing LED, D1 (or whatever load is chosen). At this setting of VR1, at temperatures above zero, the smaller resistance value of TH1 will keep the inverting input, pin 2 of IC1, above the 4.5V reference on pin 3, keeping output pin 6 negative, thus holding off the output transistor and its load.

Layout (Fig.35)

Two 7-way terminal blocks are used for this circuit, and to accommodate the integrated circuit IC1 it is best to tack or screw them on to a small piece of plywood. The 8-way dual-in-line holder should be fitted with short lengths of wire to connect with the terminal blocks. The thermistor can be located in a remote position using a 2-way terminal block and a length of twin flex.

Components for Project 11

Resistors
R1, R2   10k (2 off)

R3	1M
R4	4.7k

Potentiometer

VR1	470k lin.

Semiconductors

D1	flashing LED (see text)
TH1	thermistor (n.t.c.) 10k at 25 deg. C.
TR1	BC109

Switch

S1	SPST (on/off)

Terminal Blocks

TB1, TB2	7-way (2 off)

Miscellaneous
9V battery (PP3) and clip, 8-way d.i.l. holder, small project box, plastic-insulated wire.

Project 12 – Electronic Thermometers

The temperature-dependent resistance of a thermistor makes it the ideal candidate for use in electronic thermometers. For the most basic form of thermometer, a thermistor can be connected to a meter that is capable of reading its resistance, which is of course an indication of its temperature. It just requires a little effort, and perhaps some ingenuity, to fix and calibrate a meaningful scale. The problem with simple circuits is that they are not very sensitive, the scale does not indicate zero reading and suffers from non-linearity. An improved circuit is possible by connecting the thermistor into one of the arms of a bridge circuit. To obtain greater sensitivity, a transistor or integrated circuit amplifying stage can be used.

Ohmmeter Thermometer (Fig.36)
As shown, the resistance of a thermistor can be read directly by an ohmmeter, to give an indication of the prevailing

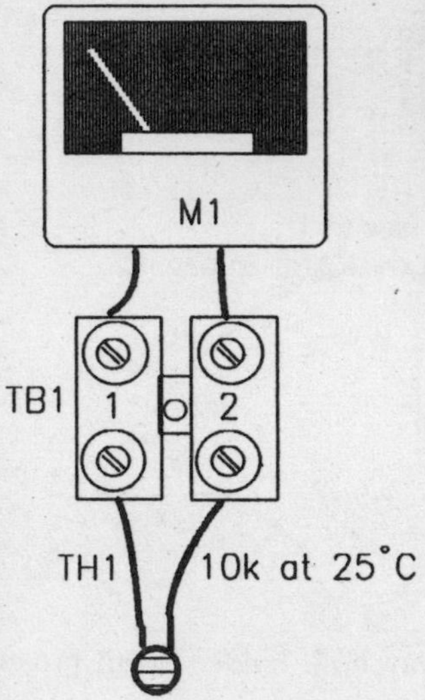

Temp. °C	Resistance
−20	67k74
−10	42k45
0	27k28
10	17k96
20	12k09
30	8k313
40	5k828
50	4k161
60	3k021
70	2k229
80	1k669
90	1k266
100	0k973
110	0k758

use lower ohms range
for greater accuracy
at higher temperatures

Fig. 36   Ohmmeter thermometer

temperature. For an unknown thermistor, the readings can be calibrated against a commercial thermometer, or by checking temperatures experimentally. For instance, freezing point (0 deg. C) can be checked by immersing the thermistor in iced water. Similarly, the boiling point of water (100 deg. C) can be readily checked. The thermistor used for the following projects was rated at 10k ohms ±1% at 25 deg. C. It was supplied with a list of all other values at 5 degree intervals from 329k at −50 deg. C, to 757.9 ohms at 110 deg. C. The values at 10 degree intervals are given in Figure 36. Armed with such a list, it is a simple matter to read off the temperature in celsius directly from a good ohmmeter, or to mark out a suitable scale.

Voltmeter Thermometer (Fig.37)
In order to measure the resistance of a thermistor using a voltmeter, it is necessary to provide an external voltage source.

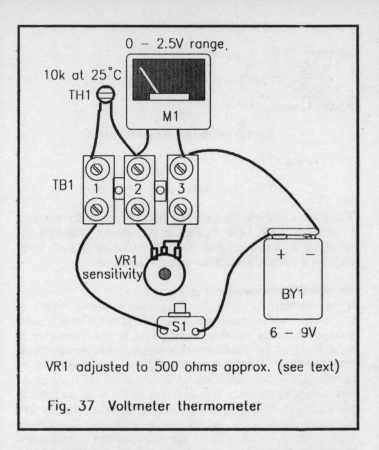

Fig. 37 Voltmeter thermometer

The value of the voltage source will be determined by the range of the meter used for temperature measurement. Some experiments were made using a 7.5V battery and a voltmeter scale of 0 to 2.5V. The resistance of TH1 and a variable resistor VR1 of about 500 ohms were wired in series, forming a potential divider across the 7.5V battery. It will be realised that as the current is the same through both resistors, by Ohm's Law, the voltage across each of them is proportional to the ratio of their resistances.

If the VR1 is adjusted to 500 ohms, then as TH1 has a resistance of 27k at 0 deg. C, freezing point equals:

$$7.5 \times 500 / (27000 + 500) = 0.136V$$

Similarly, 25 deg. C equals:

$$7.5 \times 500/(10000 + 500) = 0.357V$$

50 deg. C equals:

$$7.5 \times 500/(4000 + 500) = 0.833V$$

and, 100 deg. C equals:

$$7.5 \times 500/(1000 + 500) = 2.500V$$

This gives a guide to the spread of the scale on a voltmeter with a range of 2.5V f.s.d. (full-scale deflection). Although the voltmeter is in parallel with VR1, its resistance is sufficiently high for it to have little effect on the calculation.

Ammeter Thermometer (Fig.38)
If an ammeter is used for temperature measurements in conjunction with a thermistor, it must be in series with it and a voltage source. A variable resistor VR1 is also connected in series to adjust the sensitivity. This resistor could be adjusted to give full-scale deflection at the highest temperature to be measured, i.e. corresponding to the smallest total resistance (the maximum current). Typical points on the scale are listed in the figure. If a more sensitive ammeter is available, say 250 microamp f.s.d., a 3V battery would suffice for the voltage source. Again, by Ohm's Law, the meter current is determined by dividing the voltage source by the resistance of TH1 + M1 + VR1.

Transistor Thermometer Circuit (Fig.39)
A more sensitive thermometer is obtained by following the thermistor with a one-stage amplifier circuit. Sometimes there may be a need to observe small changes in temperature, and a sensitivity control can be used to increase the output, using the mid-scale area of the meter to good effect. The range can also be increased by shunting the output meter to double its full-scale value.

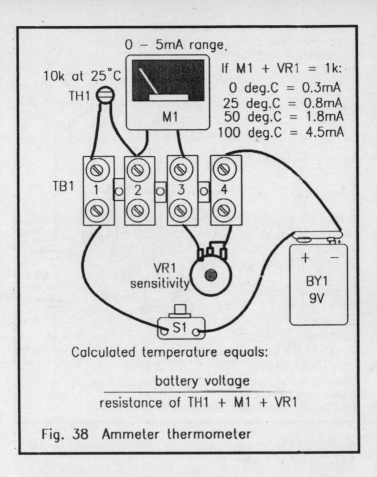

Fig. 38 Ammeter thermometer

The inside-figure text reads:

0 – 5mA range.

10k at 25°C
TH1

M1

If M1 + VR1 = 1k:
0 deg.C = 0.3mA
25 deg.C = 0.8mA
50 deg.C = 1.8mA
100 deg.C = 4.5mA

TB1 1 2 3 4

VR1
sensitivity

+ −
BY1
9V

S1

Calculated temperature equals:

$$\frac{\text{battery voltage}}{\text{resistance of TH1} + \text{M1} + \text{VR1}}$$

The base current for transistor TR1 is supplied from a potential divider across the supply rails, formed by the thermistor TH1 and the variable resistor VR1. The amount of base current supplied via R1 depends on the setting of VR1 and the resistance of TH1. As the temperature increases, the resistance of TH1 falls and the resultant increase in base current produces more collector current in TR1. This collector current is monitored by a 500 micro-amp meter in series with a limiting resistor R2. To cater for an increase in output current, a shunt

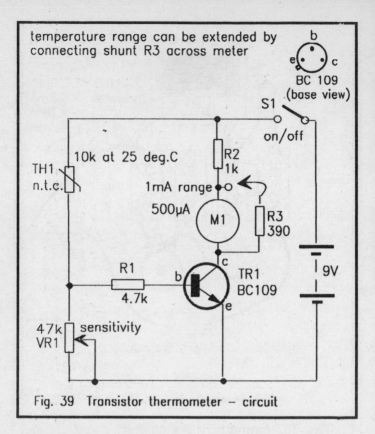

Fig. 39 Transistor thermometer — circuit

resistor R3 can be linked across the meter, effectively doubling its full-scale to 1mA.

Transistor Thermometer Layout (Fig.40)
The meter can be mounted on the front panel of a plastic project box together with the on/off switch and sensitivity control. The thermistor must also be accessible; for general purposes, a probe on a short lead would be suitable. Although the range switch is shown as a link on the 6-way terminal block, a single-pole switch would be more convenient. Although a BC109 transistor is specified, almost any small signal, low frequency npn-type can be used.

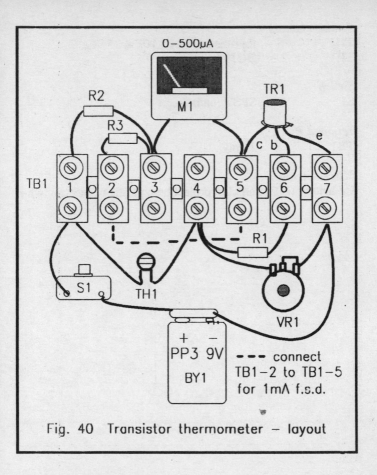

Fig. 40 Transistor thermometer — layout

Components for Project 12

Resistors

R1	4.7k
R2	1k
R3	390Ω(see text)

Potentiometer

VR1	47k lin.

Semiconductors
TH1   thermistor (n.t.c.) 10k at 25 deg. C
TR1   BC109

Switch
S1   SPST (on/off)

Terminal Block
TB1   7-way

Miscellaneous
9V battery (PP3) and clip, project box, plastic connecting wire.

Chapter 6

SOUND-OPERATED SENSORS

Microphones, the 'ears' of the electronic world, come in all types, shapes and sizes. A microphone can truly be called a transducer, as it converts sound vibrations into electrical energy. Generally, it produces only a few millivolts, but sufficient potential to be processed, amplified and fed to a loudspeaker (an output transducer) for conversion into much stronger sound waves. The most useful type for the hobbyist is the crystal microphone, which operates on the piezo-electric principle, i.e. when a wafer of crystal is flexed, an alternating voltage is produced across its faces. Piezo crystal inserts are quite suitable for the projects listed; they are cheap, give a reasonable output and are available from electronics stores and mail order catalogues. In addition, their high impedance matches easily into integrated circuits. On the other hand, dynamic, or moving-coil microphones, that employ a small coil vibrating in a strong magnetic field, are low-impedance devices and often require a matching transformer. They work on the same principle as moving-coil loudspeakers, and in intercom systems a small loudspeaker can be used to double as a microphone.

Acoustic Feedback

Unlike our two ears, microphones cannot always distinguish between wanted and unwanted sounds, although sophisticated directional and noise-cancelling microphones are available. In a crowded room we often hear what we want to hear, but the 'one-eared' mike is not always so discriminating. When using voice amplifying systems for public address, ensure that a loudspeaker is not facing a microphone, otherwise you risk a sensing problem. Noise picked up by the microphone will be amplified in the system, produce louder noise in the speaker, which in turn will be picked up again by the microphone to produce even louder noise in the speaker. This cycling action will build up until an annoying howl appears.

71

An extreme case of this occurred a number of years ago when a helicopter PA system was ordered by the Hong Kong police for air-to-ground riot control. For testing purposes, two massive 150 watt horn speakers were bolted on the side of the helicopter, unfortunately only a metre or so from the microphone. Subsequently, I had a severe problem of airborne acoustic feedback to sort out. Several microphones were tried, while observers on the airfield listened to a string of nursery rhymes and some meaningless monosyllables – human sensors still have their uses! Better screening, and either a dynamic noise-cancelling, or a throat microphone eventually solved the problem.

Here are a few typical circuits that can be activated by a microphone input.

Project 13 – Piano-forte Ranger

This circuit is basically a sound level meter, but with a musical flavour. The loudness of music, whether vocal or instrumental, is traditionally indicated on manuscript by the same symbols, ranging from very soft, pp (double-piano) to very loud, ff (double-forte). Whether there is one voice, thirty voices, a stentorion trombone, or an entire symphony orchestra, these levels are used. How loud then is forte if one or more musicians are observing a forte? As you probably realise, all is relative! Not surprising when a symphony orchestra at full throttle (fff) could produce a deafening 140 decibels of sound. All this explains the need for a sensitivity control in this meter circuit, although the scale covers only the range: pp, p, mp, mf, f, ff.

Circuit (Fig.41)
The sound is picked up by a dynamic or crystal microphone insert MIC1 and the small alternating voltage is applied via the d.c. blocking capacitor C1 to the non-inverting input of op-amp IC1. Equal-value resistors R1 and R2 provide a potential divider to bias input pin 3 to +4.5V. With no signal input, this means that the inverting input, pin 2, and the output, pin 6, are also held at +4.5V. However, sound signals from MIC1 on pin 3 are superimposed on the d.c. level and amplified depending

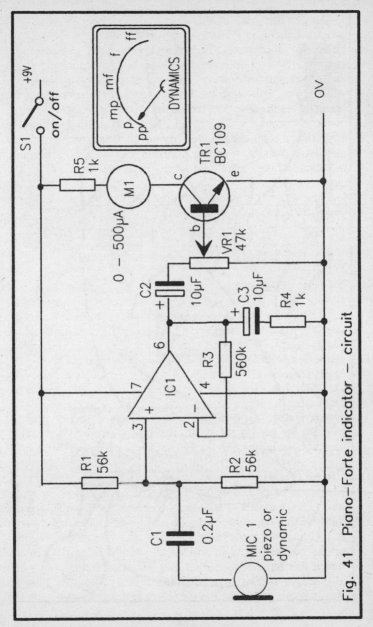

Fig. 41 Piano–Forte indicator – circuit

73

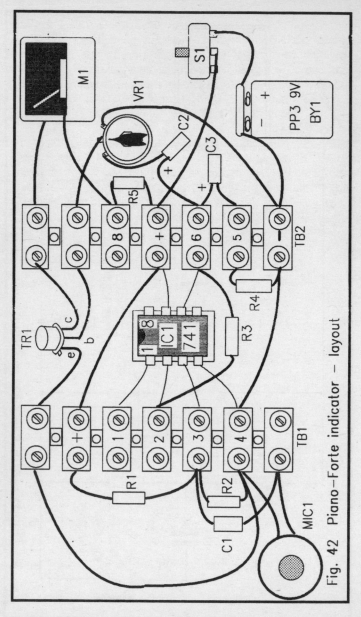

Fig. 42 Piano–Forte indicator – layout

on the gain of IC1. This is set by the ratio of R3/R4 and is approximately 560. The audio output at pin 6 is passed by the d.c. blocking capacitor C2. Depending on the strength of the sound input, number of musicians, location of microphone, etc., the sensitivity control VR1 can be set to provide a suitable output from transistor TR1 for the meter.

Layout (Fig.42)
The 8-pin integrated circuit is best accommodated on two terminal blocks as shown. If long microphone leads are used, these should be screened, especially if this is a crystal microphone, as high resistance input sources are more liable to unwanted pick-up. The scale may be calibrated to read from pp (very soft) through to ff (very loud).

Components for Project 13

Resistors
R1, R2   56k (2 off)
R3   560k
R4, R5   1k (2 off)

Potentiometer
VR1   47k

Capacitors
C1   0.2μF
C2, C3   10μF elect. (2 off)

Semiconductors
IC1   741 op-amp
TR1   BC109

Meter
M1   0 – 500μA

Microphone
MIC1   crystal or dynamic insert

Switch
S1   SPST (on/off)

Terminal Blocks
TB1, TB2   7-way (2 off)

Miscellaneous
9V battery (PP3) and clip, suitable project box, plastic-covered wire.

Project 14 – Sound-activated Relay

There are a number of useful applications for a circuit that responds to sound, and in the interests of flexibility, an output relay with switching contacts provides a suitable solution.

This circuit responds to speech, whistles, hand claps, finger clicking and taps in the vicinity of the microphone. It suggests a device for switching on lights, sounding alarms, operating small motors and mechanical devices, etc.

Circuit (Fig.43)
The front-end of the circuit, operational amplifier IC1 is identical to that of the previous project, the gain being set by the ratio of R3/R4. Again, the d.c. blocking capacitors C1, C2, C3 ensure that the d.c. bias set by R1, R2 is not affected by the microphone or the following stage. The sound picked up by the microphone is amplified in IC1 and the audio signal across VR1 is applied to the base of the emitter follower TR1. Signals exceeding the emitter-base junction and the emitter bias, switch on TR1. The resulting output across R6 triggers the gate of thyristor THY1 and its anode current operates relay RL1. This remains latched until it is manually reset by momentarily switching off S1. The 'make' contacts can be used to switch whatever output sensor is required, within the current/voltage rating of the particular relay contacts.

WARNING: In the interests of safety, no mains or high-voltage/current circuits should be connected with these simple terminal block, open-construction projects.

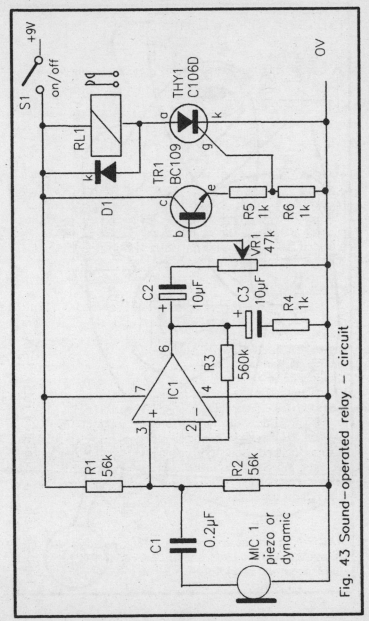

Fig. 43 Sound-operated relay – circuit

77

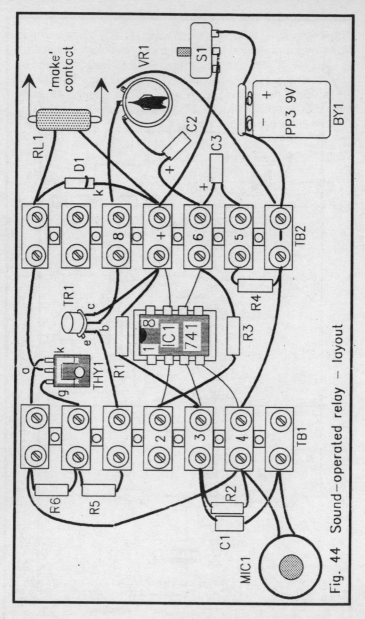

Fig. 44 Sound—operated relay — layout

78

Layout (Fig.44)

Two 7-way terminal blocks house the 741 IC, but two single TBs will probably be needed for the relay contacts. Depending on the type of relay, you may need flexible leads soldered or wire-wrapped to the contacts. The same applies to the thermistor if the existing leads are not long enough to screw into the terminal block. Make sure that the thyristor connections are fitted as shown.

Components for Project 14

Resistors
R1, R2	56k (2 off)
R3	560k
R4–R6	1k (3 off)

Potentiometer
VR1	47k

Capacitors
C1	0.2µF
C2, C3	10µF elect. (2 off)

Relay
RL1	5V reed relay or 6–12V miniature

Semiconductors
IC1	741 op-amp
TR1	BC109
THY1	C106D thyristor

Microphone
MIC1	crystal or dynamic insert

Switch
S1	SPST (on/off)

Terminal Blocks
TB1, TB2	7-way (2 off)

Miscellaneous
9V battery (PP3) and clip, suitable project box, plastic-covered wire.

Project 15 – Microphone Preamplifier

Although commercial amplifiers are often advertised as having so many watts output, it is not always obvious what level of input is needed to obtain the stated output; sometimes the output falls far short of expectations when we plug in the microphone. Generally, the microphones that give the flattest response over the audio frequency range have the lowest output. Dynamic microphones, for instance, produce only a few millivolts. This kind of situation prompted the construction of this useful one-stage preamplifier. Built into a small project box with its own battery power supply, it makes a handy stand-alone unit.

Circuit (Fig.45)
This common-emitter amplifier using the popular BC109C low-noise npn transistor, TR1, is capable of boosting the output of a dynamic microphone to several hundred millivolts. Resistor R2 provides the collector load, while the base bias is

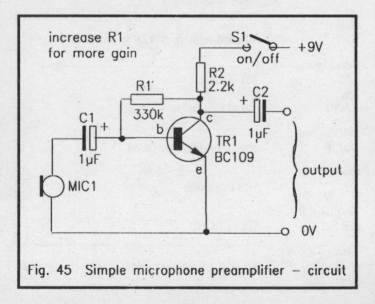

Fig. 45   Simple microphone preamplifier – circuit

obtained via feedback resistor R1. Input and output are capactively-coupled by C1 and C2 respectively.

Layout (Fig.46)
The wiring must be kept as short as possible to reduce hum pick-up to a minimum. If screened connecting cable is not available, in particular, twist the input leads together as these carry the smaller, more vulnerable signals. In the prototype, the input capacitor C1 was wired directly to a jack socket on the front panel, and the output capacitor C2 via a short lead to a jack plug.

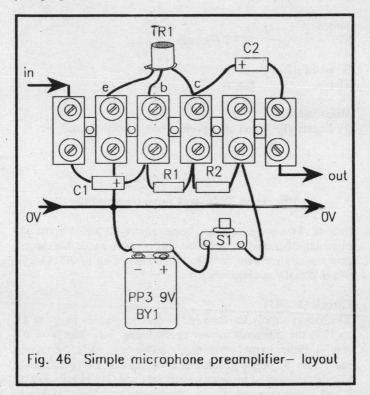

Fig. 46 Simple microphone preamplifier— layout

Components for Project 15

Resistors
R1   330k
R2   2.2k

Capacitors
C1, C2   1µF elect. 10V (2 off)

Semiconductor
TR1   BC109

Switch
S1   SPST (on/off)

Terminal Block
TB1   6-way

Miscellaneous
9V battery (PP3) and clip, project box, insulated-wire, etc.

Project 16 – General-purpose Amplifier

Several of the projects in this book require the added boost of a main amplifier, and if a suitable unit is not to hand, this modest power amplifier with an adjustable gain of up to 200 (46dB) can find many applications.

Circuit (Fig.47)
The battery supply for the LM386 can be over the range of 4V to 12V, the quiescent power drain being only 36mW at 6V (6mA). Either input can be used, in this case pin 2, the unused input (pin 3) being grounded. If a gain of 20 is sufficient, you can economise on components (R1 and C1) by leaving pins 1 and 8 unconnected. Some other gains are shown in Figure 47, obtained by juggling with R1 and C1 in series across pins 1 and 8.

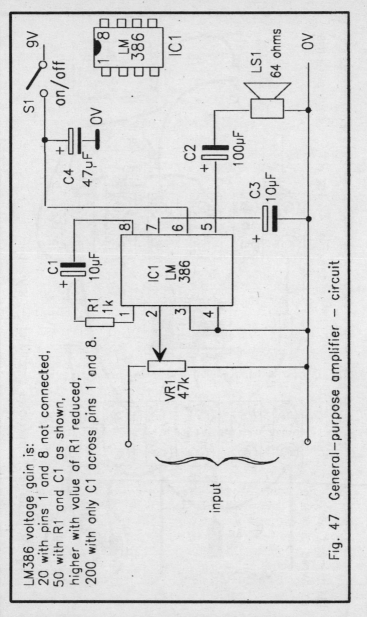

LM386 voltage gain is:
20 with pins 1 and 8 not connected,
50 with R1 and C1 as shown,
higher with value of R1 reduced,
200 with only C1 across pins 1 and 8.

Fig. 47 General-purpose amplifier – circuit

83

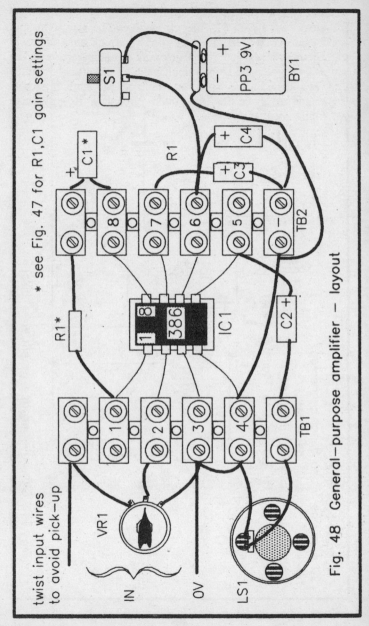

twist input wires to avoid pick-up

* see Fig. 47 for R1,C1 gain settings

Fig. 48 General-purpose amplifier — layout

84

Layout (Fig.48)

As mentioned previously, the wiring should be kept short, and input leads twisted or screened to prevent pick-up at points in the circuit where hum or feedback may be comparable with the tiny signal voltages. If the circuit tends to be unstable, reduce the overall gain. To prevent damage by static charges, remember to keep the integrated circuit in its protective wrapping until ready for use.

Components for Project 16

Resistors
R1   1k

Potentiometer
VR1   47k log.

Capacitors
C1, C3   10µF elect. 10V (2 off)
C2   100µF elect. 10V
C4   47µF elect. 10V

Semiconductor
IC1   LM386 amplifier

Switch
S1   SPST (on/off)

Terminal Blocks
TB1, TB2 6-way (2 off)

Miscellaneous
9V battery (PP3) and clip, 8-way IC holder, project box, plastic-insulated wire, etc.

Project 17 – Dalek, Voice-interrupter

Finally, in this sound sensing chapter, here is a project with light entertainment in mind. Sounds not unlike the Daleks in 'Dr Who' can be simulated by chopping audio signals at a low frequency. Dalek and Didgeridoo effects are often done using transformers in a ring modulator circuit, but for simplicity, a reasonable 'corrugated' croaking effect can be produced using the popular 555 IC running at a chopping frequency of 50Hz or slightly more.

As a bonus, if a slower speed is used, then syllables or even whole words disappear. One TV comedian makes a living out of it, without any electronic aid – it sounds like a good idea for a party piece!

Circuit (Fig.49)
This chopping circuit is designed to be inserted across the input signal path of an audio amplifier, preferably with a fairly low-

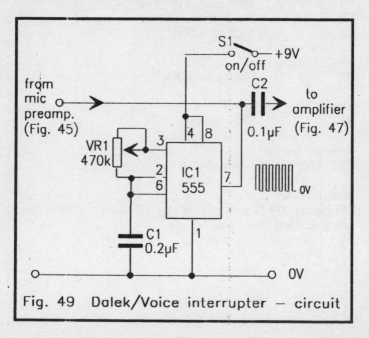

Fig. 49   Dalek/Voice interrupter – circuit

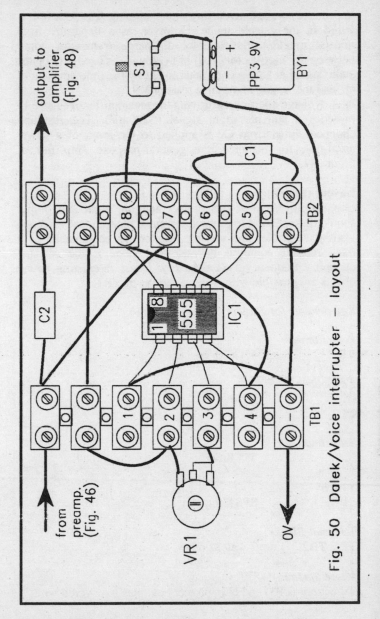

output to amplifier (Fig. 48)

from preamp. (Fig. 46)

0V

Fig. 50 Dalek/Voice interrupter – layout

impedance source to avoid any signal clipping. The 555, IC1, is wired in the astable mode. However, as a departure from normal practice, the internal discharge transistor, wired between pin 7 (collector) and pin 1 (ground), is used to chop the audio signal at a frequency determined by the time constant of C1 and the setting of variable resistor VR1.

A dynamic microphone driving the preamplifier of Figure 45 provides a suitable input signal (>100mV). The resulting chopped signal from C2 is applied to the input of a power amplifier, for instance, the general-purpose amplifier of Figure 47.

Layout (Fig.50)
Connections between this project and the input and output should be kept short to prevent unwanted pick-up; use screened leads if available. The variable resistor can be replaced by a fixed resistor equal to its measured value if the selected chopping frequency is satisfactory. Some interesting sound effects are possible with wide variations of VR1.

Components for Project 17

Potentiometer
VR1   470k lin (see text)

Capacitors
C1   0.2µF
C2   0.1µF

Semiconductor
IC1   555 timer

Switch
S1   SPST (on/off)

Terminal Blocks
TB1, TB2   7-way (2 off)

Miscellaneous
9V battery (PP3) and clip, project box, plastic-covered wire.

Chapter 7

MAGNETICALLY-OPERATED SENSORS

A small magnet brought near to a reed switch provides a simple method of closing its contacts to switch on an electronic circuit. In some cases it is more convenient than using the conventional 'make' switch described in Chapter 3. In both senses of the word, an attractive solution!

Reed Switches
The reed switch has two rhodium-plated contacts, encapsulated in a glass envelope, that make when subjected to a magnetic field. As the in-line reeds become magnetised, the overlapping free ends attract to close a switch. When used for security purposes, the reed switch can be recessed into door or window frames and magnetically activated on opening or closure as appropriate.

Reed Relays
The logical step from the magnetic reed switch is the electro-magnetic reed switch or reed relay. A high resistance coil around the reed switch enables it to be driven by a few milliamps of current from a transistor, integrated circuit, thyristor, or supplied directly by a low-voltage battery. Sealed relays are available commercially that will operate at voltages from 4V to 20V, providing both single- and double-pole switching.

Relays and Solenoids
The reed relay is a special form of the basic family of relays that clattered merrily in telephone exchanges over the years before solid-state circuits silenced their chatter. Basically, when the coil is energised, a hinged plate is attracted to a soft-iron pole-piece, the mechanical action making or breaking a set of contacts.

Solenoids are also available, consisting of a coil that operates a plunger sliding inside the former. When the coil is energised, the resulting stroke of the plunger can be used to operate mechanisms, e.g. to strike resonant bars as in door chimes, or to act as a bolt for a lock.

Electromagnetic Probes

Reed switches, relays, solenoids, like compass needles, sense magnetic and electromagnetic effects and convert them into mechanical movement. Conversely, a coil subjected to a moving or alternating magnetic or electromagnetic field produces a corresponding voltage. The tiny electromagnetic radio waves can be picked up with a few turns of wire on a ferrite rod aerial, but need rectifying and amplifying to make them audible. A multi-turn probe, such as a telephone pick-up coil, can be used as a probe to detect circuits that oscillate or generate electromagnetic fields; for instance, computers, TVs, radios, live mains cables, unshielded transformers, etc.

Tape Recorder Heads

A piece of plastic recording tape is coated with a fine layer of tiny particles of ferromagnetic powder that can be individually magnetised by passing it at a constant speed across a recording head. The head consists of a ring magnet with a gap in it that comes into contact with the tape. Briefly, when recording, audio frequency signals influence the magnetic structure of the tape particles as it is drawn across the gap in the head.

On playback, the magnetic patterns on the tape, moving over the head, induce audio frequency electrical signals into the coil, which are amplified and transduced by the loudspeaker into sound.

Project 18 – Cat-nap Alerter

This project was prompted by a TV programme stating that car manufacturers were developing a TV on-board accessory that detected when a driver was about to nod-off and gave an appropriate alarm. This sophisticated device included a video camera to monitor the driver's eye blinks. Undoubtedly, it is an important safety measure, but in a book of simple projects, there are much less expensive ways of catching someone napping. This magnetic solution can be used to show the tired motorist the 'red card', or to remind the late-night TV viewer that transmissions have ended. Test it for yourself in the comfort of your armchair when watching a particularly boring TV programme.

Circuit (Fig.51)

The transistor TR1 functions as a switching circuit. When the reed switch RS1 is within the field of a small permanent magnet, the reed contacts are closed. This means that the base of TR1 is short-circuited to the emitter and TR1 is therefore switched off. However, when the reed switch and magnet part company, the reed contacts open and base current is applied via R1 from the positive rail to switch on transistor TR1. The resulting collector current energises the piezo sounder alarm WD1.

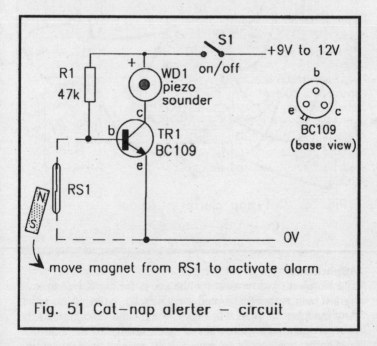

Fig. 51 Cat–nap alerter – circuit

Layout (Fig.52)

There are no special precautions needed for this simple circuit, and the five components can be screwed to the 4-way terminal block in a matter of minutes. The reed switch will need a length of flexible twin cable to extend it to a convenient working position. Soldering is the best method of connection at the reed switch end, otherwise single terminal blocks or wire-wrapping will serve. Make sure that the ends of the reed switch are not bent, as any undue force could fracture the glass envelope.

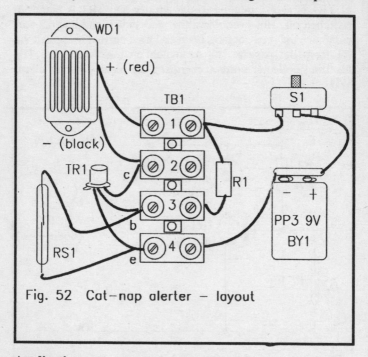

Fig. 52 Cat-nap alerter – layout

Applications

The simplest cat-nap alert for the car is for the driver to hold lightly both magnet and reed switch in the palm of the hand. Any tendency to doze will result in the hand relaxing and the magnet and reed switch will fall apart, setting off the alarm.

Another method is to tape a light magnet to the steering wheel rim at the point where the hand normally grips, and hold the reed switch lightly between finger and thumb.

Any tendency to doze on long journeys is likely to cause the wheel to wander. An additional reed switch connected in series with RS1 can be used to monitor any drift from the straight and narrow. This can be affixed to a convenient point on the steering wheel mounting panel, opposite another hold-off magnet attached to the wheel. This can be switched in circuit for motorway driving where the wheel is turned very little. Obviously, the alarm would sound when turning deliberately, but would merely serve as an assurance that the alerter is working.

WARNING!

The alerter is intended to act solely as an emergency warning that the driver is tired. In the interests of safety, at the *first* sign of tiredness a driver should pull off the road and rest.

Although specified as a cat-nap alerter, this simple circuit could be adapted for other uses.

Components for Project 18

Resistor
R1   47k

Switches
RS1   reed switch
S1   SPST (on/off)

Semiconductor
TR1   BC109

Sounder
WD1   piezo buzzer

Terminal Block
TB1   4-way

93

Miscellaneous
9V battery (PP3) and clip, small magnet, project box, plastic-covered connecting wire.

Project 19 – Intruder Alarm

The previous project could easily be adapted as an intruder alarm, by arranging a series of reed switches, each held in by a magnet, at vulnerable access points such as doors and windows. The snag would be that a door or window opened momentarily and then closed would only bring on the alarm briefly.

The circuit given below keeps the alarm activated, once triggered, by using a latching output stage.

Circuit (Fig.53)
The reed switches connected in series, normally held in by their associated magnets, short-circuit the gate connection of thyristor THY1 to its cathode, thus preventing it from firing. A break in the reed switch chain, caused by a magnet on a door or window swinging away from its reed switch, allows the supply voltage via R1 to trigger the thyristor. The anode current activates the alarm WD1, which continues to sound even if the reed switch recloses, until S1 is reset or the battery runs down.

Layout (Fig.54)
Again, the circuit layout poses no problem, but long leads will be needed to cover the access points. Single terminal blocks can be used to link the reed switches in series. Wiring must be hidden to avoid it being by-passed.

Sneaky hint to would-be intruders: Don't cut the wire, otherwise the alarm will go off!

Components for Project 19

Resistor
R1   68k

Switches
RS1, RS2, RS ...   reed switches (as required)
S1   SPST (on/off)

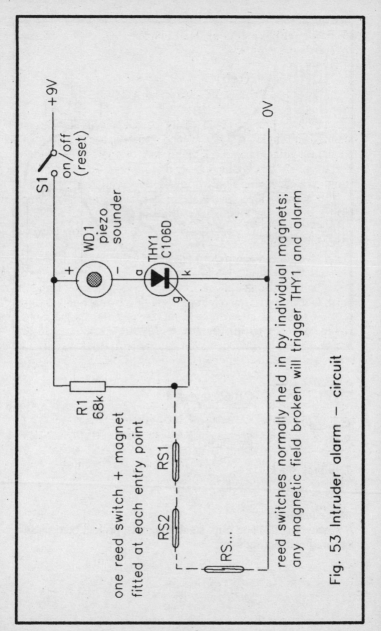

one reed switch + magnet fitted at each entry point

reed switches normally held in by individual magnets; any magnetic field broken will trigger THY1 and alarm

Fig. 53 Intruder alarm – circuit

95

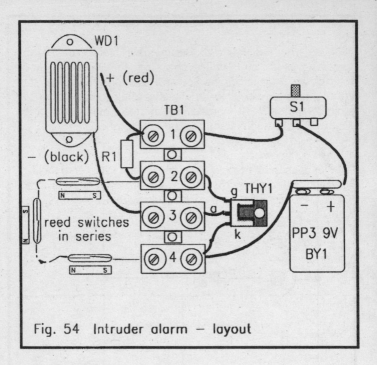

Fig. 54 Intruder alarm — layout

Semiconductor
THY1   C106D thyristor

Sounder
WD1   piezo buzzer

Terminal Block
TB1   4-way

Miscellaneous
9V battery (PP3) and clip, small magnets, project box, plastic-covered connecting wire.

Project 20 – Electromagnetic Field Detector

Whether you are trying to locate mains cable runs before knocking nails into walls, checking for electromagnetic interference from electrical accessories, simply bending your ear to a telephone conversation or recording it, this circuit can make it possible. It consists of an electromagnetic probe followed by an audio amplifier and loudspeaker.

Probes

A telephone pick-up coil or almost any iron-cored coil of several hundred turns will serve as a probe, but do experiment! The coils to hand that gave good results included a disused tape recorder head, and a 500Ω reed relay.

Circuit (Fig.55)

The probe L1 is coupled via a d.c. blocking capacitor C1 to the grounded-emitter pre-amplifier stage TR1. Resistor R1 provides

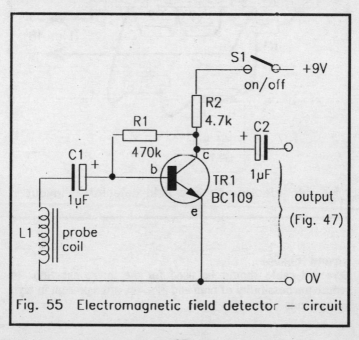

Fig. 55 Electromagnetic field detector – circuit

the feedback bias from the collector to the base. Reduce this value if the circuit is unstable. The signal voltage developed across the collector load is coupled via C2 to Figure 47 if constructed, or any suitable power amplifier.

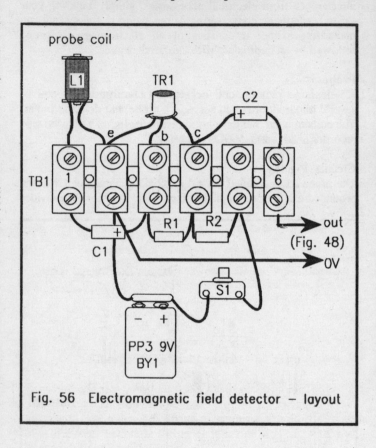

Fig. 56 Electromagnetic field detector – layout

Layout (Fig.56)
Screened cable should be used for the interconnections to reduce the possibility of hum and pick-up, often present in high gain circuits.

Components for Project 20

Resistors
R1   470k (see text)
R2   4.7k

Capacitors
C1, C2   1µF elect. 10V (2 off)

Coil
L1   telephone pick-up coil (Tandy) or see text

Semiconductor
TR1   BC109

Switch
S1   SPST (on/off)

Terminal Block
TB1   6-way

Miscellaneous
9V battery (PP3) and clip, project box, plastic-covered wire.

Project 21 – Guitar Pick-up Preamplifier

The guitar pick-up is normally a few thousand turns of fine wire wound around six small magnets, with a pole piece under each steel string. For experiment, a one-string guitar was made up using a single coil and a steel string stretched between two points, with a raised bridge at one end. As the name of the game was demonstrating sensors and transducers this adequately proved the circuit. Interestingly, it was found that a discarded tape record/playback head gave a good output signal. Furthermore, a tuning fork struck and held close to it sounded loud and clear, taking a number of seconds to decay.

Circuit (Fig.57)

The circuit of the guitar preamplifier is basically the same as that of the previous circuit, apart from the coil differences and the experimental addition of the two diodes, D1 and D2, across the bias resistor R1. There are germanium diodes that conduct slightly on high signals and provide a small measure of positive and negative clipping. Although this distorts the waveform, it tends to remove some of the initial twang that characterises the guitar and gives more emphasis to the middle frequencies.

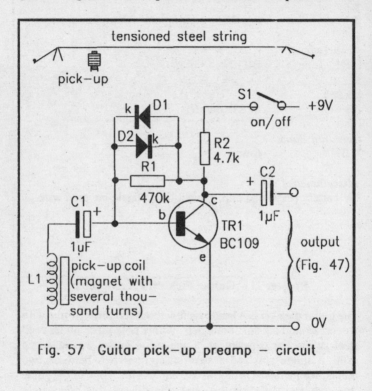

Fig. 57 Guitar pick—up preamp — circuit

Layout (Fig.58)

Make sure that the diodes are fitted cathode to anode, and anode to cathode, so that one clips the positive peaks and the other clips the negative troughs of the audio signal. These may be

100

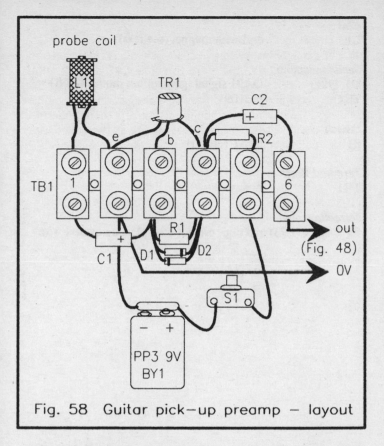

Fig. 58 Guitar pick—up preamp — layout

omitted if clipping is not required. Again, keep interconnecting leads short and screened if possible.

Components for Project 21

Resistors
R1   470k (see text)
R2   4.7k

Capacitors
C1, C2   1µF elect. 10V (2 off)

Coil
L1   coil with magnet (see text)

Semiconductors
D1, D2   OA91 signal, germanium diodes (2 off)
TR1   BC109

Switch
S1   SPST (on/off)

Terminal Block
TB1   6-way

Miscellaneous
9V battery (PP3) and clip, project box, plastic-covered wire.

Chapter 8

MOTION-OPERATED SENSORS

Sensors that are capable of detecting movement are not all primarily motion-operated sensors. In this book they would fit comfortably under some of the other chapter headings. One of the standard tests by opticians is to blow puffs of air into the eye to check its response. Although you could hardly call the eye a motion-operated sensor, for the purpose of that particular optical test it serves as such.

Here are a few sensing devices that operate in response to movement.

Mercury Tilt Switch
A ball of mercury encapsulated in a glass tube is free to roll about and bridges two contacts when the tube is tilted. Any movement relative to gravity can be arranged to either make or break the contacts depending on the attitude of the switch. An inert gas in the sealed tube prevents arcing.

A practical application for this angular movement detector is as a car intruder alarm. Any deviation in the angle of the car on its suspension caused by an intruder can easily be made to sound an alarm. Some kind of adjustment would be needed when parking on a slope, and a delay or remote switch off would be necessary to allow the legitimate driver undisturbed access.

Ball-bearing Switches
Mercury tilt switches are perhaps a little expensive to be used in quantity, but the same principle of a metallic ball bridging two contacts can be adopted using ball-bearings. These are ideal for making electronic pin-board games. In these games, the movement of the ball is extended and sensed by a number of contact springs.

Light-dependent Resistors (LDRs)
Variations in movement causing changes in light patterns enable these electronic eyes, LDRs, described in Chapter 4, to

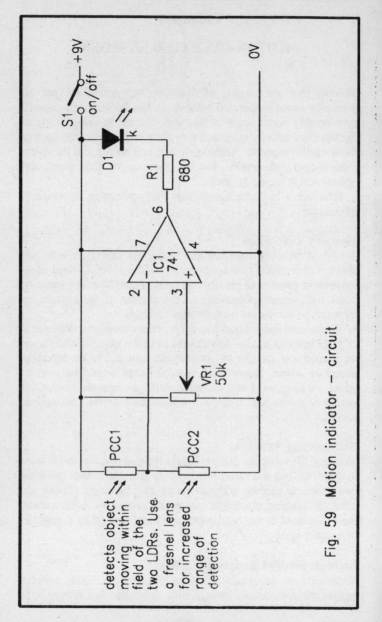

Fig. 59 Motion indicator – circuit

detects object moving within field of the two LDRs. Use a fresnel lens for increased range of detection

104

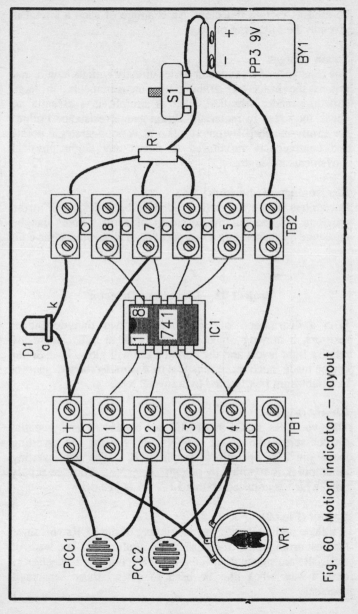

Fig. 60 Motion indicator — layout

be used as motion detectors. An example of such a circuit is given in the following project.

Strain Gauges

The resistance of a conductor varies directly with its length, and this is the basis for strain gauge measurements. In large structures under vibration, such as aircraft, it is essential to check for stress in materials. Strain-gauge resistance bridges are firmly attached by epoxy resin at various strategic points and continuously monitored to detect any slight physical movements in length.

Electromagnetic Sensors

Encounters of the magnetic kind have been described in the previous chapter, but measurement of earth tremors can be measured by suspending a magnet over an electromagnetic coil.

Project 22 – Movement Detector

With a distribution of light over the two light-dependent resistors, a moving object in front of them will change the relative light levels and the output LED will glow. This circuit can be made much more sensitive by enclosing the two sensors in a light-tight box fronted by a fresnel lens.

Circuit (Fig.59)

The two LDRs, PCC1 and PCC2, are connected as a potential divider across the power supply rails, feeding the inverting input, pin 2 of operational amplifier IC1. The non-inverting input, pin 3, is supplied by potentiometer VR1 from the supply rails, which is adjusted so that LED D1 is just off.

Layout (Fig.60)

A little experiment with the positioning of the LDRs will show the best arrangement for a particular application. The leads of the LDRs are shown connected into TB1, but two 2-way blocks or a 4-way block can be used to extend these sensors if necessary.

Components for Project 22

Resistor
R1   680 ohms

Potentiometer
VR1   50k lin.

Semiconductors
IC1   741 op-amp
D1   LED
PCC1, PCC2   ORP12 light dependent resistors (2 off)

Switch
S1   SPST (on/off)

Terminal Blocks
TB1, TB2   6-way (2 off)

Miscellaneous
9V battery (PP3) and clip, 8-way d.i.l. holder, plastic-covered wire.

Project 23 – Flip-flop Game

This project uses a 555 timer IC in its bistable mode. The bistable is a two-stage device connected so that the output of each stage is coupled to the input of the other. A signal on one input registers on the other output and is stored in memory until the alternate input is triggered and flips it over to the other output – hence the name flip-flop.

This action suggests a basis for a number of security circuits and board games, exploited in other books in the 'Terminal Block Projects' series, but here is a simple cricket game that simulates net-practice. As most readers will realise, there are two small movement sensors in cricket that indicate whether the stumps have been hit by the ball, namely the two bails! In this board game, played on a miniature version of a cricket pitch, the sensors are the three stumps. A ball-bearing is rolled

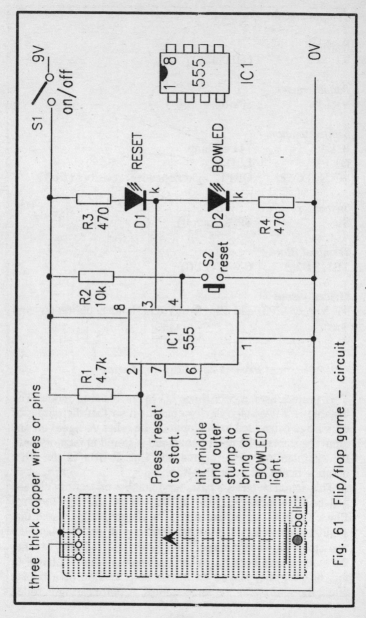

Fig. 61 Flip/flop game — circuit

108

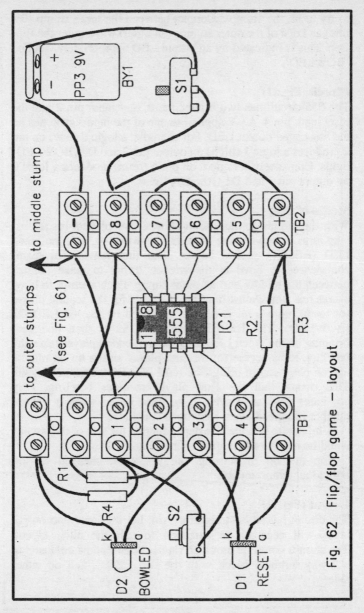

Fig. 62 Flip/flop game — layout

to try to hit the stumps. Contact between the inner stump (0V line) and one of the outer stumps (an input) will trigger the flip-flop. This is indicated by an output LED appropriately labelled 'BOWLED'.

Circuit (Fig.61)

The 555 circuit has two inputs, the trigger input pin 2 and the reset input pin 4. A 0V applied to one of the inputs switches on the associated output LED. For example, a logic 0 (low) on pin 2 produces a logic 1 (high) on output pin 3 and D2 (BOWLED) lights. Conversely, a logic 0 on pin 4 (reset) produces a logic 0 on output pin 3 and D1 (RESET) lights.

Modes of Play

With the circuit configuration shown, two players (or teams) take turns to bowl at the wickets. At switch-on, D1, the green LED (RESET) should be on. The first bowler (or team) commences to bowl at the wicket, trying to make contact between the middle and an outer stump. Each attempt to bowl scores one run against him, i.e. it counts for the second player (or team), until a hit is scored, indicated by the red LED D2 (BOWLED). The RESET pushbutton S2 is then operated, bringing on the green LED D1, and the second player takes the bowling. Runs accrue for the first player until a hit on middle and an outer stump brings the red LED (BOWLED) on again. This means that the first player resumes bowling. Play continues until all players have been in, or when a limited number of agreed overs have been concluded.

A miniature bat, the size depending on the size of the stumps could be used to enliven the proceedings.

The method of scoring can easily be changed to suit individual requirements.

Layout (Fig.62)

The circuit layout is straightforward, but the input and output leads will need to be extended to suit the pitch layout. The stumps could be mounted on the three middle connects of a 7-way terminal block with the two LEDs fitted on either side.

Components for Project 23

Resistors
R1	4.7k
R2	10k
R3, R4	470 (2 off)

Semiconductors
IC1	555 timer
D1	LED (green)
D2	LED (red)

Switch
S1	SPST (on/off)

Terminal Blocks
TB1	7-way
TB2	6-way

Miscellaneous
9V battery (PP3) and clip, 8-way d.i.l. holder, plastic-covered wire, additional terminal blocks as required.

Chapter 9

RESISTANCE-OPERATED SENSORS

Apart from the light-dependent resistors and thermistors already discussed in earlier chapters, where the sensing is primarily dependent on a physical source of energy, there are sensors that operate an electronic process dependent on the value of resistance present in a circuit. Resistance, in the electrical sense is a passive ingredient – it won't do very much without those active ingredients, voltage and current.

How can the property of resistance be employed in practical sensing circuits?

- A resistance-operated sensor can be a fingertip that bridges two adjacent contacts by skin resistance, providing a path for minute currents that will in turn trigger a circuit.

- A potentiometer can be rotated to a point where the resistance selected provides sufficient voltage to operate a process.

- A variable resistor can be turned so that the series value of resistance is reduced to allow the correct amount of current to flow in a circuit.

Project 24 – Visual Alerter

Often, a monitoring situation calls for a silent attention-getter instead of the noisy clanging of bells. For instance, a visual alerter could find favour in a public library, in other noise-abatement locations or as a door alarm for those with hearing difficulties.

As the visual alerter project is introduced in this chapter a touch resistance-operated sensor is used for the input, but a pushbutton could be substituted depending on the application.

113

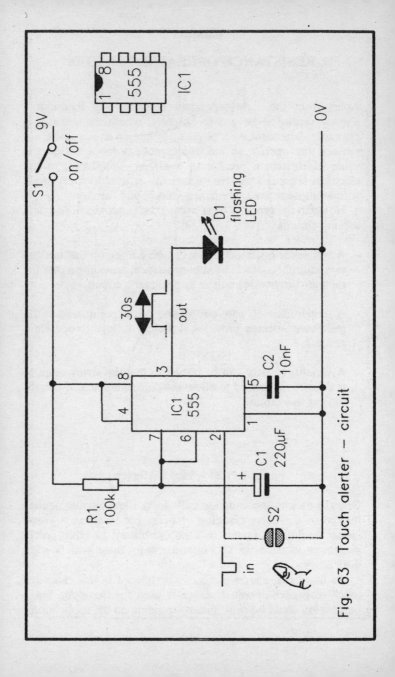

Fig. 63 Touch alerter — circuit

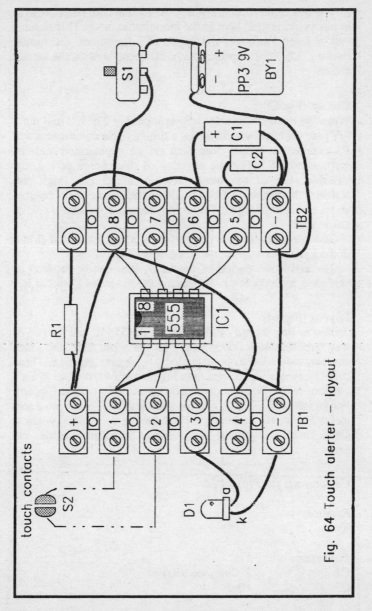

touch contacts

Fig. 64 Touch alerter — layout

The ubiquitous 555 timer, a popular choice for other projects in this book, is used here in the monostable mode. This ensures that a brief touch on the input will illuminate the output flashing LED for approximately 30 seconds with the circuit shown.

Circuit (Fig.63)

When the contacts between trigger input pin 2 of IC1 and pin 1 (0V) are bridged by a fingertip, a timing cycle commences and C1 charges at a rate dependent on its capacitance and the resistance of R1. For the duration of this charge period, the unstable state of the monostable, output 3 goes high and activates the flashing LED, D1. When the charge on C1 reaches about 6V, it discharges. The output on pin 3 returns to 0V, its stable state.

The rate of flashing is controlled by a tiny integrated circuit in the LED and is about two flashes per second.

The activation period of the LED (30s) can be reduced or extended, by reducing or increasing the values of C and/or R.

Layout (Fig.64)

An 8-way breadboard can be used for the 555 IC and the two 6-way terminal blocks. Depending on the application, the touch contacts may need to be extended to a remote position. These could be two brass-headed drawing pins mounted close to each other, or two adjacent copper strips of printed circuit stripboard. For an intruder alarm, it may be sufficient to connect pin 2 to a metal object, for example, a door handle or a metal window catch. Touch switches are also useful as activators in games and toys.

Components for Project 24

Resistor
R1   100k

Capacitors
C1   220µF (see text)
C2   10nF

Semiconductor
IC1   555 timer
D1   flashing LED

Switches
S1   SPST (on/off)
S2   touch contacts (see text)

Terminal Blocks
TB1, TB2   6-way (2 off)

Miscellaneous
9V battery (PP3) and clip, 8-way d.i.l. holder, plastic-insulated wire.

Project 25 – Musical Slide

This circuit is clearly resistance-operated. Using the movement of a variable resistance it is easy to slide up and down a musical octave or more. Certainly more notes than you can glissando on a trombone slide! Add a simple oscillator circuit and a pushbutton and you have an interesting electronic musical instrument. Any kind of resistance-capacitance oscillator could be used for this project, but as the 555 timer chip has featured in other projects it can serve here in its free-running mode as an astable multivibrator.

Circuit (Fig.65)
The pitch or the frequency of a note sounded by the loudspeaker depends on the resistance of VR1 and R1 and the capacitance of C1. With C1 and R1 fixed, the different notes of a scale are obtained by moving the slider of VR1. Pushbutton S1, basically an on/off control, is used to start and stop the notes. In this way, those glissando sliding effects in between the selected notes can be omitted or controlled. Although C1 is fixed, it is possible to drop the overall pitch an octave by switching a capacitor of the same value across it – capacitors in parallel add. Conversely, a capacitor of equal value switched in

117

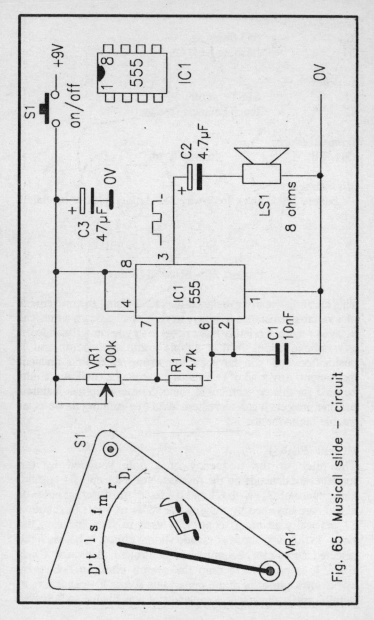

Fig. 65 Musical slide — circuit

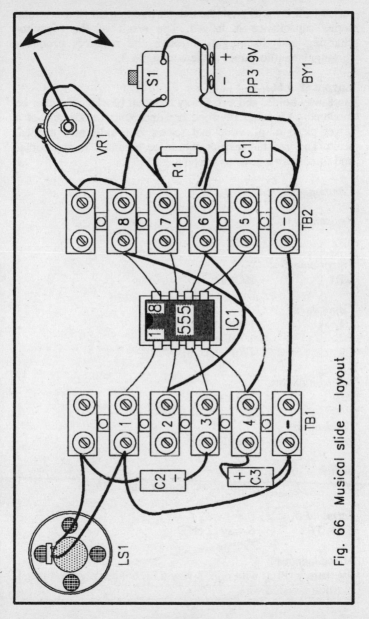

Fig. 66 Musical slide — layout

series with C1 will push the overall pitch up an octave – total series capacitance is halved. The result of the capacitor charging and discharging through the resistors produces rectangular audio waves at the output pin 3.

Layout (Fig.66)
An 8-way holder and two 6-way terminal blocks can either be mounted on a small plywood breadboard or on the rear of a larger piece of plywood that serves as a calibrated musical scale. The variable resistor should be mounted in one corner and fitted with a lever to sweep the scale.

Components for Project 25

Resistor
R1   47k

Potentiometer
VR1   100k lin.

Capacitors
C1   10nF (see text)
C2   4.7µF elect. 10V
C3   47µF elect. 10V

Semiconductor
IC1   555 timer

Loudspeaker
LS1   8Ω miniature

Switch
S1   pushbutton, non-locking (on/off)

Terminal Blocks
TB1, TB2   6-way (2 off)

Miscellaneous
9V battery (PP3) with clip, 8-way d.i.l. holder, plywood panel, plastic-insulated wire.

Project 26 – Water-level Limit Alarm

Simple tasks like filling a cup or a jug with water can become a major operation if your sight is poor. Although this handy circuit is intended as a water-level limit measuring device for a blind person, it can be adapted for other uses, such as an overflow alarm, or a rain sensor, etc.

Its operation depends on the fact that the presence of impurities in water make it conductive.

Circuit (Fig.67)

Two thick copper wire sensors of different lengths balanced over a cup or jug are bridged when water is poured to the level where both are immersed. The conductive path of the water and the resistance set by VR1 act as a potential divider across the 9V supply, that supplies base current to transistor TR1 via R1. The variable resistor VR1 is adjusted so that the base current switches on TR1 when the sensor probes are just immersed. This occurs when the base voltage exceeds 0.7V.

Layout (Fig.68)

The sensing probes can be attached to a separate terminal block, with some provision for it to balance across the top of the cup or other container. A 4-way terminal block could be used, with short wires screwed into the outer terminals, and bent outwards to straddle the rim of the container.

Components for Project 26

Resistor
R1   1k

Potentiometer
VR1   500k

Semiconductor
TR1   BC109

Sounder
WD1   piezo buzzer

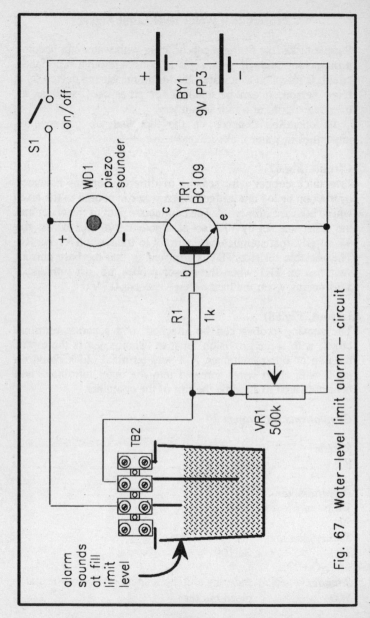

Fig. 67 Water-level limit alarm – circuit

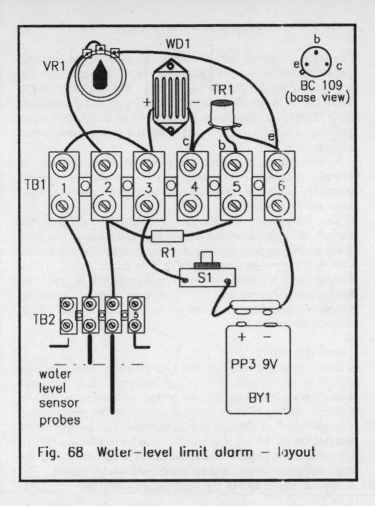

Fig. 68 Water—level limit alarm — layout

Terminal Blocks

TB1	6-way
TB2	4-way (see text)

Miscellaneous

9V battery (PP3) and clip, suitable container, plastic-insulated wire.

Project 27 – Gas Detector

The sense of smell was briefly mentioned in the opening chapter, and when we are aware that some toxic gases are not to be sniffed at, it is comforting to know that an electronic gas sensor can do the sniffing for us. In this respect, the gas detector really deserves a chapter on its own, but as it is a resistance-operated sensor, it is included with the resistance-operated sensors.

It is designed to detect the presence of such gases as propane, methane, iso-butane, natural gas, etc., to prevent hazardous conditions building up, in storage depots, ships' holds and road vehicles.

The resistance of certain oxides change according to the number of oxygen atoms absorbed. The sensor has two platinum-wire resistor heating elements, one of which is coated with this oxygen-sensing material. The ohmic value of this element varies according to the oxygen content of the gas. The other element, identified by a coloured dimple, serves to compensate for changes in temperature and is used in bridge circuit measurements.

Circuit (Fig.69)

In this simple gas detector, the two elements form a bridge circuit together with two fixed resistors, R1, R2, and potentiometer VR1. Initially, the bridge is balanced by VR1 to give zero reading (0V) on the millivoltmeter. The meter output is proportional to the gas concentrations. The bridge circuit operates on 2V to 3V d.c. supply, which must be capable of delivering about 160mA. The meter could be replaced by an op-amp comparator circuit and an alarm indicator if desired.

Typical output figures for gas concentrations are:

Gas	0.1%	0.5%
methane	5mV	30mV
propane	12mV	60mV
iso-butane	14mV	70mV

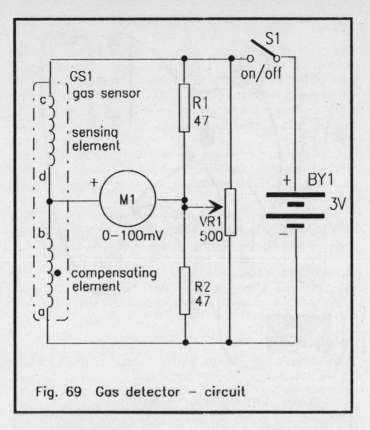

Fig. 69 Gas detector — circuit

Layout (Fig.70)

The layout is straightforward, apart from the mounting of the gas sensor. The four pins are 8mm long and ideally should be plugged into suitable holders. However, they could be soldered or wire-wrapped. The pin orientation is shown with respect to the coloured marker, which lies between the compensation winding (ab).

Components for Project 27

Resistors
R1, R2   47Ω (2 off)

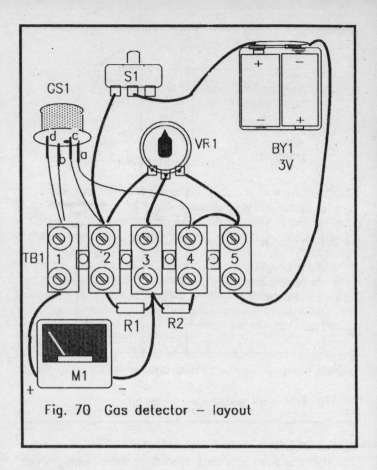

Fig. 70 Gas detector — layout

Potentiometer
VR1   500Ω lin.

Gas Sensor
GS1   resistive (RS Components 286-614 or
                   Maplin FM87U)

Terminal Block
TB1   5-way

Switch
S1   SPST (on/off)

Miscellaneous
3V d.c. source, plastic-insulated wire, etc.

Project 28 – Pressure Mat Relay Alarm

Intruders are well and truly on the carpet when they unwittingly step on to an underlay pressure mat. Commercial versions of these mats, available to fit under carpets and stairs, provide a short-circuit input to an alarm circuit when subjected to pressure.

They are sometimes fitted in shop doorways to register by audible or visible means that a potential customer has entered. However, when used to detect intruders, some kind of latching circuit is needed to sustain the alarm when the unwanted caller has stepped off the mat.

The following circuit is suitable for both applications, the holding circuit contacts being omitted, or switched out of circuit when used for monitoring genuine callers.

Circuit (Fig.71)
The relay coil RL1 is connected in series with the pressure mat across the 6V supply when S1 is switched on. The weight of a foot short-circuits the mat and energises the relay.

Contacts RL1/1 close and connect the lower end of the relay coil to the 0V line. These contacts continue to hold (latch) in the relay even if the pressure is removed from the mat.

The other contacts RL1/2 energise the bell or buzzer by connecting the lower end to the 0V line.

Because of the hold contacts (RL1/1), the alarm continues to ring until the circuit is reset by momentarily switching off S1.

If the latching facility is not required, disconnect the RL1/1 contacts, or connect a 'break' switch in series with them.

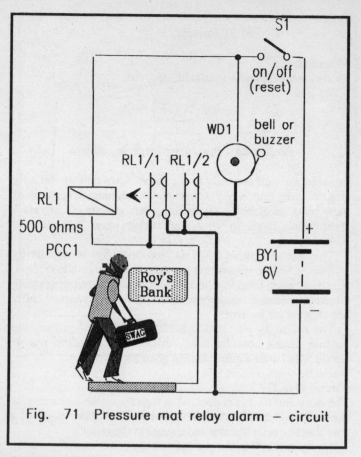

Fig. 71 Pressure mat relay alarm — circuit

Layout (Fig.72)

The layout diagram shows the base connections of a miniature 6V double-pole, double-throw, relay that is capable of switching up to 4A. Note that two of the connections are not needed for this particular application. For clarity, the circuit diagram Figure 71 shows only the two relay 'make' contacts that are used. The pin lengths are only 3.5mm so will need to be soldered or wire-wrapped.

Alternatively, a double-pole reed relay is also available with a 5V, 500Ω coil that will switch 1A max.

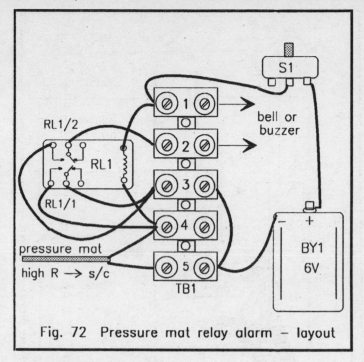

Fig. 72   Pressure mat relay alarm — layout

Components for Project 28

Switches
RL1   6V, DPDT changeover relay (FJ42V), or
                5V, DPST reed relay (JH15R)
S1   SPST (on/off)

Sounder
WD1   bell or piezo buzzer

Terminal Block
TB1   5-way

Miscellaneous
6V battery, Maplin pressure mat (YB91Y) or stair pressure mat
(FK79L), plastic-covered wire.

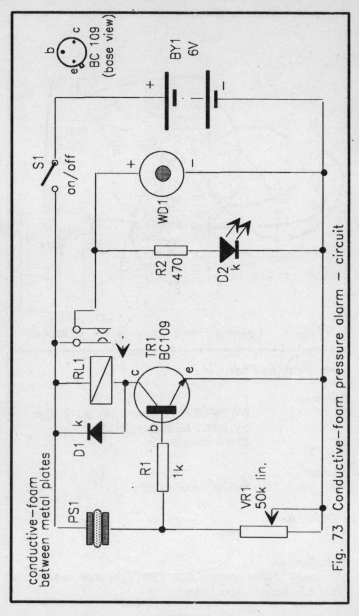

Fig. 73 Conductive-foam pressure alarm — circuit

130

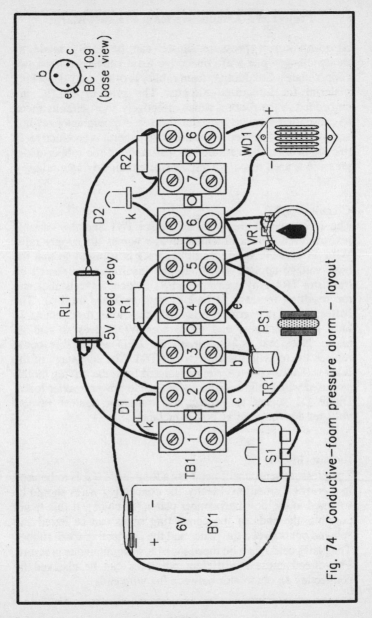

Fig. 74 Conductive–foam pressure alarm – layout

Project 29 – Conductive-foam Pressure Alarm

A do-it-yourself pressure sensor can be easily made by sandwiching a piece of conductive-foam rubber between two copper plates. Conductive-foam rubber is often used as packing material for integrated circuits. The pins of the IC are embedded in the rubber, which effectively short-circuits them, so preventing damage by static charges. An ohmmeter reading across a strip of rubber will indicate whether it is conductive. In this application the variation in resistance of the rubber under pressure is used to switch a transistor circuit driving a relay.

Circuit (Fig.73)

The resistance of the pressure sensor PS1 and the variable resistor VR1 form a potential divider across the supply rails. With no pressure exerted on PS1, VR1 is adjusted so that the base voltage applied via R1 is just insufficient to switch on transistor TR1. Any pressure on PS1 reduces its resistance and the resulting increase in base current switches on TR1. The collector current energises relay RL1 and closes the contacts. In turn, LED D2 lights and the buzzer WD1 gives an audible alarm. Note that in this circuit the LED and buzzer could replace the relay in the collector of TR1. The advantage of the relay is that its contacts can be isolated from the driving circuit and used with a higher capacity battery to power heavier loads. Diode D1 serves to protect the transistor against reverse voltages due to the relay coil inductance.

Layout (Fig.74)

The pressure sensor will need extra long leads if it is to be used in a practical situation. Ideally, the connecting wires should be soldered to the polished copper plates (or coins). If this is not possible, the ends of the connecting wires can be bared and splayed out between the plates and the conductive-foam rubber. The plates could then be taped together without undue pressure. The effectiveness at different pressures can be checked by connecting an ohmmeter between the wire ends.

Components for Project 29

Resistors
R1   1k
R2   470

Potentiometer
VR1   50k lin.

Semiconductors
D1   1N4001 silicon diode
D2   LED
TR1   BC109

Sounder
WD1   piezo buzzer

Switches
RL1   5V reed relay
S1   SPST (on/off)

Terminal Block
TB1   8-way

Miscellaneous
6V battery and connections, PS1 pressure sensor, small project
box, plastic-insulated wire.

Chapter 10

VOLTAGE/CURRENT-OPERATED SENSORS

Generally speaking, in the previous chapters, transducers have been introduced that primarily change non-electrical physical quantities such as heat, light, sound and movement into electrical signals. Here, in the last two projects, the active electrical quantities, voltage and current, are available, ready and waiting to be sensed for pleasure.

Project 30 – Battleships and Submarines

The title 'Battleships and Submarines' will no doubt conjure up that popular 'end-of-term' school game, a relaxing pastime that launched us into the holiday break. This electronic version is somewhat simplified, but broadly speaking follows the same lines as that pencil and paper game. It was a game for two players, each with identical charts divided into grid references. Unseen by the other, each player pencilled in ships at a chosen location on his or her chart. Players then took turns to locate their opponent's craft by stating grid references. These points were carefully logged to ensure that turns were not lost by repeating them. The first player to locate all their opponent's ships was the winner.

Simple Electronic Version
This simple version has only sixteen grid references (contact pins) so the number of craft needs to be limited to one, or perhaps two. There is only one chart, i.e. the front panel (see Fig.75), with its 4×4 matrix of sixteen pins representing the grid references. Initially these pins are all given an electrical charge and the ships are 'set' by discharging selected pins on this pattern of electrical charges. Alternate pins are coded either red or green, which allows a degree of variation in the method of play.

The circuit details are given later, but a basic understanding of how the charge patterns work is useful at this stage. The

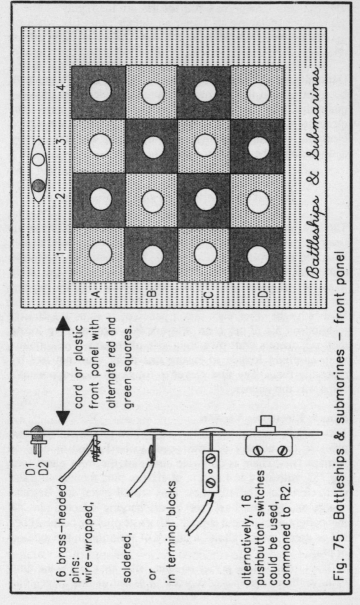

4 3 2 1

A
B
C
D

Battleships & submarines

card or plastic
front panel with
alternate red and
green squares.

D1
D2

16 brass-headed
pins: wire-wrapped,

soldered,

or

in terminal blocks

alternatively, 16
pushbutton switches
could be used, commoned to R2.

Fig. 75 Battleships & submarines – front panel

136

eight pins in the alternate red squares are the inputs of one 8-input logic gate, which lights an output red LED when all inputs are positively charged. Similarly, when all eight pins in the alternate green squares are positively charged, the output of a second 8-input logic gate lights a green LED. From this, it will be realised that all eight inputs of one colour must be positive to obtain an output. With all sixteen inputs charged, both output LEDs will glow. From this condition, each player in turns sets up a ship (or ships) in turn by touching the discharge probe on selected pins of his or her own colour. Once a coloured pin is discharged, the LED of that colour is extinguished. A battleship is set up by discharging two diagonally adjacent pins of the player's colour, a submarine, by discharging one pin.

In the simplest game, each player in turn subtly discharges say, a battleship and a submarine or two. Both players would then use the charge probe in turn to try to locate their opponent's ships. Success is indicated when the appropriate coloured output LED glows. The skill is in remembering which contacts you have already charged with the probe. The plodder may methodically start on the colours in the first row and press on to the end, but after a time it is possible to anticipate what your opponent is likely to set up. Notice that the LED on the charge probe will flash momentarily when touching a discharged pin. If the output LED does not glow, the flash is a useful indication that you have located a ship, but there are still ships, or parts of a ship, to be found. For instance, you may have located half a battleship and it could help to locate the other half. Alternatively, you could have located a submarine, and there's another sub or a battleship elsewhere. With this simple version, players could declare the type and number of their craft beforehand, or just the number of agreed squares they occupy.

Game Variation
It is relatively easy to locate a ship when there are only sixteen grid pins, especially if a craft occupies only the adjacent diagonal pins of one colour. However, a more skilful variation emerges where one player occupies the table at a time, as in snooker. The player can use all adjacent pins of any colour,

137

diagonal or lateral, for defining ships. For a two-pin battleship there are 24 lateral positions and 18 diagonal position it could possibly occupy. Note that when lateral pins are used to define a ship it takes both the red and green LEDs out.

In this version the first player charges the sixteen pins, then sets up the discharge patterns, and the second player has to attempt to locate the ships using as few goes as possible. At some stage one of the output LEDs will glow, signalling that the player should now go for the other colour. When both lights are on, the number of attempts should be recorded. The second player then initialises the panel using the charge probe, and sets up discharge patterns for the first player to probe for the ships. The number of attempts a player takes to restore the 'win' lights is recorded each time, the one with the lower overall score after an agreed number of games is the winner.

Circuit (Fig.76)

The circuit shown uses two 4068 CMOS 8-input NAND-gates that perform identical rôles. The basic operating principle of a NAND-gate is that when all inputs are positive (logic 1), the output goes negative (logic 0). If we consider IC1 for example, a positive on input pins 2, 3, 4, 5, 9, 10, 11 and 12 force output pin 13 low. As a result, the red LED (D1) is energised via the current-limiting resistor R1 from the +9V rail. Similarly, a positive on all the eight inputs of IC2 forces pin 13 low and energises the green LED (D2). The positive voltages could be applied to the inputs via switches, but for this application a 'probe and contact' method was preferable to limit connections. However, as it is necessary for all inputs to be positive at the same time to produce a logic 0 on the output, an electrolytic capacitor (C1 – C16) is connected to each input. In addition to holding the charge applied by the probe via R2 and D3, the capacitor also serves to tie the input low in the discharge state; left open, CMOS inputs can float high and give false results. The probe LED, D3, is included to indicate the state of the capacitors during a game; the LED will glow momentarily when the charge probe contacts an input capacitor in the discharged state. This gives an indication that a ship (or part of a ship) has been located.

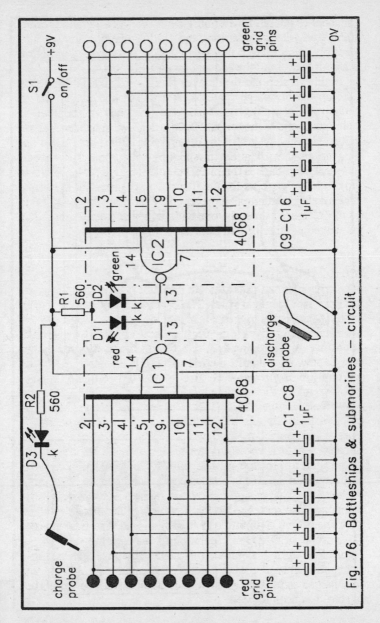

Fig. 76 Battleships & submarines – circuit

139

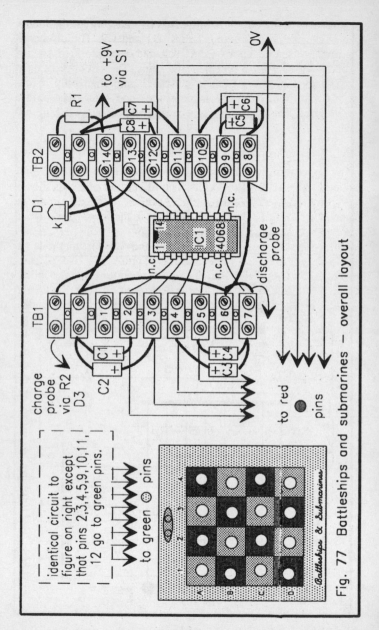

Fig. 77 Battleships and submarines — overall layout

140

As stated, the circuit is initialised by charging all the inputs to bring on the two output LEDs, D1 and D2. The discharge probe is used to short-circuit selected capacitors to set up discharge patterns to represent the ships. The circuit uses only microamps until an LED is activated, and then only a few milliamps until an LED is activated, and then only a few milliamps. The capacitors can be discharged by switching off S1.

Layout (Fig.77)
Two 9-pin terminal blocks are more than adequate to make up one of the NAND-gate circuits. The full circuit of IC1 is shown in the overall layout diagram. Another identical circuit is necessary for IC2. The pin connections to the front-panel layout are as indicated in this figure.

A view of the front panel, and the various methods of connecting to it, are illustrated in Figure 75. Use plastic-covered stranded wire for the interconnections for flexibility and to avoid short-circuits. The leads to the two output indicator LEDs, appropriately mounted in a boat-shape, can be extended by an additional terminal block if necessary. There is no need to duplicate the two probes or R2, D3.

Components for Project 30

Resistors
R1, R2   560Ω

Capacitors
C1–C16   1μF elect. 10V (16 off)

Semiconductors
IC1, IC2   4068 8-input NAND-gate (2 off)
D1   LED (red)
D2   LED (green)
D3   LED (yellow)

Switches
S1   SPST (on/off)

Terminal Blocks
TB1–TB4   9-way (4 off)

Miscellaneous
9V battery (PP3) and clip, probes, wire and suitable panel
arrangement with 16 pins (brass pins or paper-fasteners).

Project 31 – Simple Radio Receiver

In this final project, a modern version of the early crystal set, a
tuned coil of thin insulated wire is used to sense minute electromagnetic radio waves that have been generated back at the
transmitter. These are then detected by a germanium diode to
produce audio frequencies, which are then converted into sound

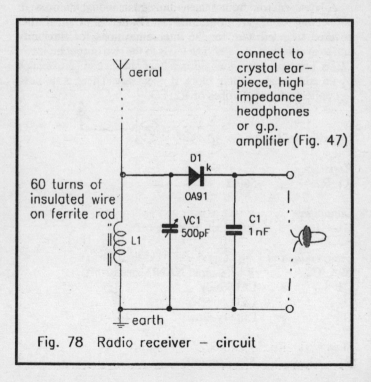

Fig. 78 Radio receiver – circuit

energy by a transducer, e.g. earphones, or amplified to feed a loudspeaker.

Notice that this is the only circuit in the book that doesn't have a battery. It is powered by courtesy of the BBC, or whatever other stations you can pick up – the prototype was also powered by several stations in the Common Market.

Circuit (Fig.78)

The coil L1 in parallel with the variable capacitor VC1 forms a resonant circuit that can be tuned to pick up radio waves around the ferrite rod. The radio frequencies (r.f.) selected by the tuned circuit are applied to the sensitive germanium diode D1 where they are demodulated, i.e. only the positive swings of the r.f. are passed by D1 and so a varying audio frequency (a.f.) signal is produced. The small capacitor, C1, traps any radio frequencies to earth, but does not affect the audio signals, which are passed to the earpiece (or an amplifier). Experiment with the amplifiers of Projects 15 and 16 if these have been constructed.

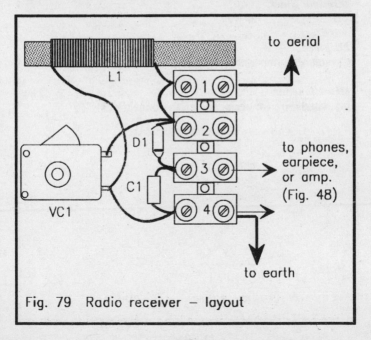

Fig. 79 Radio receiver – layout

Layout (Fig.79)

The layout calls for little comment, except to say that signal strength will be greatly increased if a good aerial and earth are fitted. Make a good earth connection to a cold-water pipe or to a copper rod in the ground. A generous length of wire attached to the top coil connection and mounted as high as possible works wonders. Otherwise, those two sensors on either side of your head will have to work overtime!

Components for Project 31

Capacitors
VC1   500pF variable tuning capacitor
C1   1nF plastic foil

Semiconductor
D1   OA91 point-contact germanium diode

Terminal Block
TB1   4-way

Earpiece
Crystal high impedance (Maplin)

Miscellaneous
Insulated wire for aerial and earth connections.

Please Note

Babani Radio, Electronics and Computer books should be available from all good Booksellers, Radio Component Dealers and Mail Order Companies.

However, should you experience difficulty in obtaining any title in your area, then please write directly to the Publisher enclosing payment to cover the cost of the book plus adequate postage.

If you would like a complete catalogue of our entire range of Radio Electronics and Computer Books then please send a Stamped Addressed Envelope to:

BERNARD BABANI (publishing) LTD
THE GRAMPIANS
SHEPHERDS BUSH ROAD
LONDON W6 7NF
ENGLAND